GW00385095

THE SEVERN BORE

This little book, however unworthy, is a small tribute in a form I think he would like, to the memory of my friend and companion of many walks and talks on Severn side,

the late

PHILIP STURDY

THE SEVERN BORE

FRED ROWBOTHAM

Foreword by
Sir Peter Scott

DAVID & CHARLES
NEWTON ABBOT LONDON NORTH POMFRET (Vt)

British Library Cataloguing in Publication Data

Rowbotham, Fred
The Severn bore.—3rd ed.
1. Bores (Tidal phenomena)
2. Severn, River (Wales and England)
I. Title
551.47'08 GC376

ISBN 0-7153-8508-0

First published 1964
Second edition 1970
Third edition 1983

and printed in Great Britain
by Redwood Burn Ltd., Trowbridge, Wilts.
for David & Charles (Publishers) Limited
Brunel House Newton Abbot Devon

Published in the United States of America
by David & Charles Inc
North Pomfret Vermont 05053 USA

CONTENTS

ILLUSTRATIONS

IN TEXT

THE ILLUSTRATIONS

The author would like to thank the following for permission to reproduce pictures: Nos. 1 and 9, Gloucester *Citizen and Journal*; 2, 3 and 9, Mr Hugh Walwin; 4 and jacket, Mr C. W. F. Chubb; 10, Mr Frank Chamberlayne; 12, Mr Russell Adams; 14, Dr J. Allen (from *Scale Models in Hydraulic Engineering*, Longmans, Green & Co.).

FOREWORD

by

SIR PETER SCOTT

I am a Londoner by birth, and a countryman by adoption. The first countryside to adopt me was the Fen Country of Norfolk and Lincolnshire. Only since 1945 have I been adopted by the country which flanks the River Severn at its mouth. Like many a convert I yield to none in my allegiance to the green fields of Gloucestershire. Each winter's morning White-fronted Geese cross in front of my window in great skeins, as they swing up from the estuary, over the sea wall and down into the grass fields to feed. The wild ducks pour down at first light onto the pond in front of the house or into the secret seclusion of the ancient duck decoy, and the tame birds swim all the year round in the pools of the Wildfowl Trust. In summer I hang in my glider high above the Cotswold edge and look out across the unrivalled panorama of the wide Vale below, across to the distant Black Mountains beyond the Forest of Dean and past May Hill to the Malverns. The whole scene is dominated by the silver snake of the river winding down past Gloucester and into the Bristol Channel.

My home lies opposite that indefinable part of the estuary which is not quite river, not quite sea. From the house, at the times of Spring tide, we can hear the flood as it rushes in over the sand on its way into the funnel-mouth of the river which will turn it into a bore. Over our sands the little wave is only a foot high at most, but up in the narrows round the great bend it will gradually build up into a breaking roller more than six feet high, a strange and fascinating sight which draws hundreds of spectators on those special days of equinox when it is expected to be at its highest and best. Why and how does it happen? This I have wanted to know in detail ever since the first day I saw it, but no such details had I been able to discover until I saw the manuscript of Fred Rowbotham's book. Now I find that the anatomy and origins of a bore are no less fascinating than its appearance, and that they are most lucidly described in this book—the first book ever to be devoted to this particular kind of bore. It is the biography of a bore, and as the Severn is the longest river in Britain, and sports the biggest bore, there could be no better example to select for such a biography.

I am particularly pleased to have been asked to write this foreword and to wish the book success not only because its subject is fascinating, but because it has given me a new insight into the Severn Estuary which has been the centrepiece of my special interests during the last fifteen years—the noble expanse of brown sand and grey mud, blue water and green salting beside which I have made my home.

PETER SCOTT

Slimbridge, 1964

Chapter 1

TALK OF A RIVER

The man on the bank kicked idly at an empty tin, rusty and half hidden among the wrack and debris left high, but not so very dry, by a recent tide.

'D'you mean to tell me the tide gets right up here?' he asked.

I told him it comes higher than that. He gazed thoughtfully at the water a good ten feet below, where stones protect the bank at Minsterworth.

'Marvellous,' he said. 'Marvellous the tides you get on the Severn!' How right he was!

Inevitably our conversation reached the bore. He wanted to know about it, and we were there for ages, for, as he said before he left, 'There's more to it than you'd think.'

In writing the story of the Severn bore, hoping to produce something helpful and of interest, I am impelled at once to get the worn-out pun over and done with for a start, never to appear again in these pages—or, I would hope, anywhere else. So with apologies to Isaak Walton and his immortal guide to the art of angling, I trust this little work will not merit the title 'The Compleat Bore' in any sense other than the one intended.

Britain is almost devoid of spectacular natural phenomena of the active sort and, on balance, is the pleasanter for it. An odd glacier or geyser here and there might not be unwelcome, but who wants volcanoes, earthquakes, typhoons, cyclones and the like? The true midnight sun just fails our most northerly outposts, and we of the further south usually happen to be spending the evening indoors, all unwitting, while the aurora gives one of its rare displays in the night sky overhead.

But we have the bore—that relentless moonchild, the eerie wave that glides, sweeps and crashes its way upstream through the lower reaches of the Severn when tides are high. Not that the Severn is the only river in the British Isles to boast something of the sort, but on no other does the wave attain the same proportions of both height and width together. If any estuary has the shape and tides necessary for the initial stages of bore-making, then bores will be found on such rivers flowing into it as have the right features to complete the process. Thus, as well as the Severn, certain other rivers running into the Bristol Channel have bores. On some they are hardly discernable, but Somerset's River Parrett has a quite substantial wave. In the same way the Humber tide is the parent of bores on the Yorkshire Ouse and on the Trent, called in the latter case the 'eagre', while the tides of the Wash have similar effects on the Great Ouse and other tributaries. Further north, in Border country, the upper reaches of Solway Firth are the domain of yet another British bore—the one described so dramatically by Sir Walter Scott in *Redgauntlet.*

In her classic novel *John Halifax, Gentleman,* Mrs Craik, who knew the Severn well and lived at Rose Cottage in the Gloucestershire village of Amberley, used the Trent name 'eagre' for the Severn bore at Tewkesbury, a town she called 'Nortonbury' in her book. But seek no bore at Tewkesbury nowadays, for nothing worthy of the name has run upstream of Gloucester since weirs were built across the river a hundred years ago. Certainly a high tide reaches Tewkesbury with a sudden on-set; but the real bore—never.

The name 'bore', as applied to the tidal phenomenon, appears to be derived from the Scandinavian or Icelandic 'bara', meaning a billow, wave or swell, whereas 'eagre', otherwise rendered 'eager' or 'aegir', probably comes from the Old French word *aiguere*—water or sea. We find yet another spelling of the word in Jean Ingelow's old poem, 'The High Tide on the Coast of Lincolnshire, 1571—'So farre, so fast the eygre drave'.

Even apart from Mrs Craik's fiction, the Severn wave has not always been called the bore. I have a book published in 1795 and inscribed on the title page *England Delineated; for the Use of Young Persons.* The said Young Persons are asked to note that the powerful tides of the Bristol Channel 'enter the mouths of the Severn and its tributary streams with a rapid influx; and, rolling on with a lofty head, received from our earliest historians the name of the Hygra'—a name with a classical ring about it and presumably deriving from the Greek *hygros,* of which the translations 'wet', 'damp' or 'moist' are wonderful understatements. I think *hygra* a good name and one we should prefer to 'bore' when we got used to it.

A footnote in the second volume of Thomas Harral's *Picturesque Views of the Severn,* published in 1824, states:

> 'The word Boar is by some derived from the British "Bur", signifying "indignation", "violence", or "tumult". Though the orthography of the words is different, their pronunciation is the same. Hygre, or Eager, on the other hand, has been traced to the French "Eau-guerre", or "water-war".'

Has any other word such wide variety of rendering as 'eager', 'eagre', 'aegir', 'eygre', 'hygre', 'hygra'? and I suspect the name of the Severn trow *Higre* had more to do with the bore than the Bible.

The bores of the Severn and Trent respectively were very much like those of France's Seine and Gironde, but the Seine's bores have become fewer and less powerful since its estuary has been progressively re-aligned. The French version of 'bore' is *barre,* or sometimes *mascaret*—a pretty name when properly pronounced, meaning 'an eddy of water'.

Away in distant India we find a bore on the Indus and others on various arms of the Ganges delta, principally the Hooghly and Brahmaputra. They are much like the Severn bore in height. But far away in China rolls the mighty bore of the Chiang tang kiang, reputed to be by far the biggest in the world. In Brazil, the *pororoca* invades the Amazon and its lower tributaries, while other bores of some magnitude are found on rivers flowing into the Bay of Fundy, that of the Petitcodiac river of New Brunswick being the best known in the New World.

Having paid our brief respects to the world's largest bores, and hoping to have slighted none, let us return to the river Severn.

In a book like this we should talk of the river in its own idiom, so let us clear away any ambiguity concerning words and expressions we are bound to meet. There may appear, for instance, something Irish in speaking of 'spring' tides that come in the autumn. We all know, I imagine, that 'spring' tides are big ones. We know too that big tides occur in the spring of the year, at the 'vernal equinox'—the 'green time of equal nights'. But when applied to tides, the word 'spring' has nothing to do with the season but is an adjective derived from the verb 'to spring', meaning 'to leap up high'. So all high tides are 'spring' tides, or 'springs', as we call them for short, whatever the season.

We often use the word 'tide' to denote, not a single flow and ebb, but a whole sequence spread over a group of days in which tides increase to a maximum and die away again. The same sequence may also be called a 'spring', using the word in a collective sense this time.

If you hear a river man say 'The tide shoots on Wednesday', do not be anxious; he means that Tuesday's tide will be the lowest of that particular group and on Wednesday the tides will begin to grow again, building up to the 'top of the tide' seven days hence. The 'top of the tide' is not high water, but the maximum tide of the fortnightly cycle, after attaining which the tide is said to 'break' and become smaller on each of the seven succeeding days. Low tides, of course, are 'neap tides', or just 'neaps', often pronounced 'neps'.

In addition to being the reverse of ebb, the word 'flow' has a meaning closely akin to high water. Tides are the river man's units of time. His Time Table is the Tide Table, and for him High Water is a specific time of day. When one might say 'The tide has another twenty minutes to rise before high water' the time by the river man's clock is 'Twenty minutes to flow'. Later, when he sees the water has ceased to rise, he says 'It's just about flow'.

Universally, of course, the flowing or incoming tide is 'flood tide', but, as in the case of 'flow', the word 'flood' has acquired an alternative application denoting a moment of time in the tidal day. It is the time when a new tide begins to flow or rise at any particular point. Thus, with a bore-tide, 'flood' is the moment when the bore passes the place in question.

'Head' is loosely used as an alternative to 'bore', but is more particularly applied to the first wave only of the bore. One can say 'The tide had a good head', or 'The bore had a good head'. Both will be understood. In the same way 'flood's head' is another name for the bore, especially for the leading wave and more especially if the leading wave is breaking. One hears the expression, 'It was a good bore, but it didn't have a head'—not the only instance of froth being called a 'head'!

The term 'tide wave' will crop up many times in this book, most frequently when dealing with the causes of the bore. A tide wave is not a bore, neither is a bore a tide wave. The term 'tide wave' must be kept exclusively for the tide itself, which is in fact a vast wave, as we shall see. Tide wave is the same as 'tidal wave', but in journalism and common parlance 'tidal wave' is usually employed to denote any surge of the sea other than a tide! Whether caused by a meteorological disturbance, an earthquake or an atomic explosion, we always read of a 'tidal' wave. Such surges do sometimes interact with tide waves, but fundamentally they are not tides and should be called by the Japanese word *tsunami,* or *seiches.*

A tide that 'didn't flow her mark' failed to reach the height predicted in the Tide Table, while one that exceeds prediction has 'over-topped her mark'. With a different shade of meaning, a tide is said to have 'made its mark' immediately the level starts to fall after high water, whether it reached predicted height or not. It begins to show a wet mark on banks and walls. In a way, the moment when a tide 'makes its mark' is not quite the same thing as the commencement of the ebb —certainly not of the ebb stream—because in the river and upper estuary the water continues to flow upstream for an appreciable time after the level has begun to fall.

In a river the term 'freshwater' is not generally used in its chemical sense or as opposed to the salt or brackish water brought in by the tide, nor is it the normal downward-flowing water. It denotes the additional flow resulting from rather more rain than usual and 'fresh' has more of the meaning of 'something new'. When the river, without any tidal effect, is running six feet above its normal or 'summer' level, it is said to contain six feet of freshwater, or more briefly, six feet of 'fresh'. There are three degrees of fresh: a relatively small rise is a 'freshet', a larger one a 'fresh', while one that overflows the banks is a flood, minor or major according to degree.

On the subject of flooding, why do people speak of rivers in flood as having 'burst their banks'? The only possible excuse for using the expression is when artificial flood-banks are breached. Otherwise a river simply 'overflows' or 'comes out of' its banks; or just 'floods'.

To conclude this short glossary, I should mention a couple of place names having alternative pronunciations. The bore can be seen on the outskirts of Gloucester from Telford's famous bridge at Over. You will not be wrong if you pronounce 'Over' as spelt, but the alternative 'Oover' is often heard. Then there is Awre, which I advise you to pronounce 'Oar', as being more generally used than the local 'Aar'. But whichever you choose to employ, be careful not to say 'Awe' for 'Oar', or 'Aah' for 'Aar', for you are in the West of England where consonants are given a measure of their real value—if not an over-dose!

(2) *Near the upstream end of Minsterworth*

(3) *The bore breaks on the Denny Rock at Minsterworth*

Chapter 2

THE COURSE AND CAUSES OF THE BORE

The telephone caller nearly floored me. He wanted to know where the bore starts. If 'start' implies an exact commencement, then the bore does not start; like another Topsy, it just grows! I suppose it could be said to have its beginnings where the incoming tide from the Atlantic first feels the constriction and rising bed of the Bristol Channel. It develops in the sand-locked channels of the Severn's lower estuary, and is fully grown when it has run upstream into the relatively narrow inland river.

I have watched the bore's growth from the air, noted the first tangible swell and followed its changing character through adolescence and maturity to final extinction at Gloucester. Looking down on the vast banks of mud and sand which at low water half fill the broad estuary opposite Avonmouth, the first indication of the incoming tide is the advance over the lowest sands of a sheet of water fronted by the thinnest of white lines—a little wave barely two inches high. The sands are so flat that the rapidly rising tide spreads quickly, pushing its little wave along faster than you could get away from it on foot if taken unawares. As yet there is no visible swell on the water in the deep channels, but as the vanguard of the tide moves further upstream it acquires just a trace of a roll, or rather a succession of three or four rolls—long, smooth, very shallow unbroken waves.

Up to Sharpness the channel varies greatly in width and depth from place to place. Where it is deep and wide the slight swell almost loses its identity, only to re-form in more confined reaches, while the little white wave spreads wide upon its flanks, though often lagging well behind.

Once past Sharpness the bore soon begins to form. It enters the long straight run to Awre, negotiates the Noose, and emerges to crash headlong on to the rocks at the foot of Hock Cliff, as though failing to sense the sharp turn westward into the lower arm of the Horseshoe Bend. But from a turmoil and confusion that can be heard a mile away on a still night, it soon re-forms, though sometimes not before a part has broken away and turned back seawards down the Frampton channel, only to collide with an errant bore coming up, which had branched off the main head into a more tortuous by-way nearer Sharpness. This phenomenon depends on the configuration of the sandbanks, and because they change over the years may be absent for long periods.

Meanwhile, the main bore, re-formed, is running upstream close under the Overton shore past Brick Hills before swinging across the estuary towards Box Cliff, from which bold point it hugs the outer bank all round the Horseshoe Bend, passing Bullo, Newnham, Broadoak and Westbury up to Garden Cliff. Then, re-crossing to the eastern side, it heads for Pridings by the shallow channel over Broad Stones, though part may run up the Stype by Arlingham Warth if that channel is open. Once over, the bore clings to the eastern shore past Framilode and Epney, to run heavily against Longney Crib before deciding which way to go through Longney Sands.

Between Longney Sands and Rosemary Point the river narrows and the sands diminish. Estuarine characteristics give way to those of an inland tidal river, so before it reaches the Severn Bore Inn (previously the Bird-in-Hand) at Minsterworth the bore is confined solely by normal river banks. There is no sand and the Severn is barely a hundred yards across. Here at last is the bore as most people understand it. Nevertheless it was well worth seeing in the estuary below, with one flank sweeping high along the shore and the other spreading out across the sands.

From Minsterworth to Gloucester the river is much the same width all the way, and the bore retains the same general characteristics throughout this part of its journey, climbing around the outer side of bends and breaking to some degree over shallows when the river is low.

We have followed the bore nearly to its doom. At Lower Parting, close to Gloucester, it splits in two upon the lower point of Alney Island, that area to the west of the city enclosed between the East and West Channels. The part taking the West Channel has a nearly straight run to Maisemore, passing on the way under a succession of bridges close together at Over, including Telford's famous masonry arch, now standing isolated, then through Maisemore bridge before slumping into the wide channel in which stands Maisemore weir.

No thunderous crash of waters marks the meeting of the bore against the weir. Indeed, the sudden silence is more prominent. The waiting spectator has heard nought but the roar of the weir, to which his ear has become accustomed as it does to the ticking of a clock. The bore's approach has been seen but not heard above the weir's incessant drone. Then —silence! Two sources of tumultuous noise have quelled each other; the effect is eerie. Suddenly the birds can be heard, or the wind in the trees. We speak without shouting and the Cathedral chimes may come clearly to the ear.

But a big bore does not die without a struggle. Presently the waters of the tide are surging upstream over the drowned weir (or, in the exquisite natural poetry of our local speech, 'over the drownded weir'). Forming a modest roller at their head they forge on to Upper Parting, at the upper end of Alney Island.

Meanwhile the bore that entered the East Channel at Lower Parting, to skirt the other side of the island, has similarly quelled and overtopped a corresponding weir at Llanthony and is running upstream with a strong surge towards reunion with its slightly better half at Upper Parting.

But the East Channel is nearly twice as long as the West Channel, so the remnant of the western bore has arrived at Upper Parting first and split with much confusion, most of it turning up the Long Reach towards Tewkesbury, while part runs down the East Channel and may go as far as the one time Globe Inn at Sandhurst before meeting its tardy brother face to face. After a swirling struggle for supremacy the upward tide inevitably wins, and soon the whole flow is making hard for Tewkesbury.

In the reach above Gloucester the onset of the upward flow is quite sudden when tides are very big. Boats feel a little surge but there is nothing one could call 'a bore worth seeing'. High tides will rise over Tewkesbury's weir at Upper Lode and reverse the flow for a mile or so above. The effect of a very big tide can be seen occasionally even as far upstream as the toe of Diglis weir at Worcester, where the river, though still flowing downward, may rise nine inches or a foot. Such an effect is called a 'quarage' and is not a true tide, but merely the result of the river's flow being checked by the rise in level of the lower portion of the reach. Thus ends the life-journey of the Severn's bore and tide.

Many of those who profess to know will tell you that bores are caused by high tides. To be kind, one might accept that as a half-truth, because there are no bores without high tides; but, to be honest, the statement is a downright falsehood. The bore is part and parcel of the tide, so it cannot be caused *by* the tide, for no effect can be its own cause. All open rivers that meet the sea would have bores if high tides were the cause.

A bore is an undular surge wave formed at the foremost part of a tide that has run into a channel of particular shape and proportion, both in plan and in the slope of its bed. The easiest way to acquire a general conception of the creation of bores is by visual demonstration. No doubt most of us sometimes bring miniature bores into being by one means or another. For instance, you must have noticed the ripple that

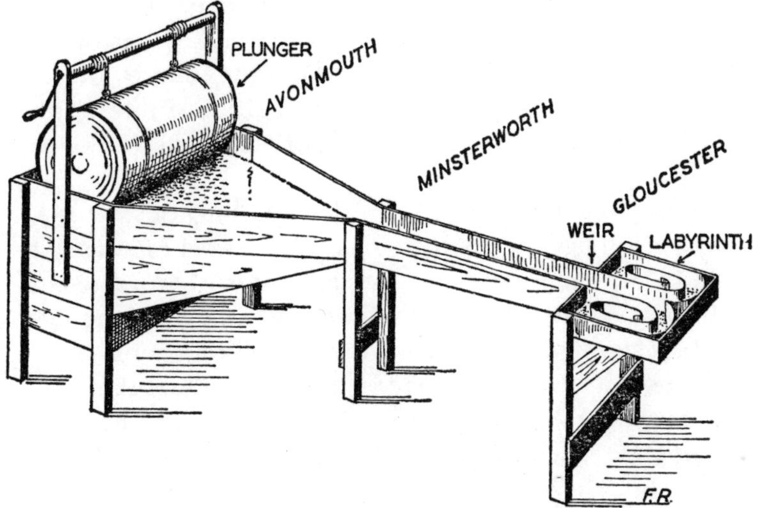

Fig. 1—Model to demonstrate how bores are created

travels up a gutter containing a little water when you suddenly pour in more water. That ripple was a tiny bore made in most respects like the Severn bore.

To demonstrate on television how bores are created I made a model having in simplest form the same elements of shape and proportion as exist in a river that produces bores (Fig. 1). Essentially the channel must be 'funnel-shaped' as in Fig. 2,

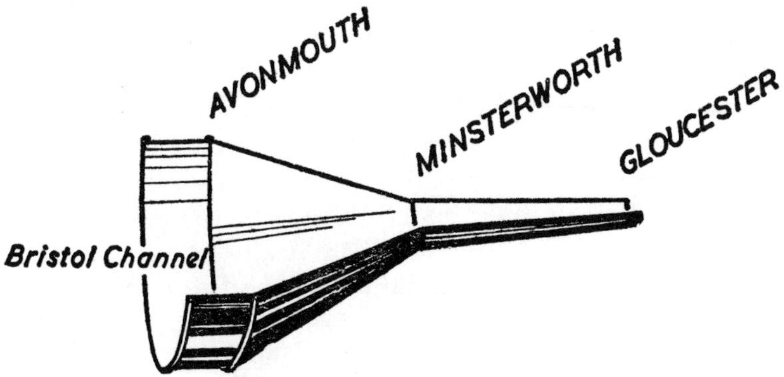

Fig. 2—The funnel shape of the Severn estuary

where the deep wide mouth represents the upper part of the Bristol Channel, with the Severn estuary rapidly narrowing and shallowing towards the neck where the stem is joined. The stem represents the Severn between about Minsterworth and Gloucester, where the river is of fairly constant width and the bed has little or no fall.

The working model (Fig. 1) has the same essential features. When the plunger at the bottom end is lowered the water it displaces rises and moves up the tapering part to represent the incoming tide. This 'tide', at first only a heave of the surface, becomes a pronounced wave as it approaches the neck. You can see it being, as it were, squeezed up. Once the 'tide' has entered the stem part of the model we see the true bore.

Primitive though it may be, this model reproduces not only the bore but at least two other features of Severn tides. When we withdraw the plunger the water runs back to simulate the ebbing tide and it can be seen that although downstream of the neck the water is running back, the bore continues to travel forward up to 'Gloucester'. This is exactly what happens in the river. While the bore is rolling up from Minsterworth, the tide is ebbing hard at Sharpness, and by the time it reaches Gloucester there is nearly an hour's ebb at Sharpness; in fact the tide is running back at all places up to Epney.

An interesting feature, that. Here we have a length of river —Sharpness to Gloucester—which at one and the same time, for a limited period, is flowing downwards at both ends and upwards in the middle! (Fig. 3). The upward-flowing middle section is the tide, headed by its bore, and it travels up the Severn rather like a match-stick shooting up the barrel of a toy gun; the match-stick is pushed hard for a short distance by the spring, then continues on its course alone while the spring retracts. We say it is 'projected'. That is why I call the upper part of the Severn tide a 'projected' tide when it travels to Gloucester and beyond as a free off-shoot detached from the true ocean tide that gave it birth and imparted initially the force by which it runs. At the upper limit of our model the

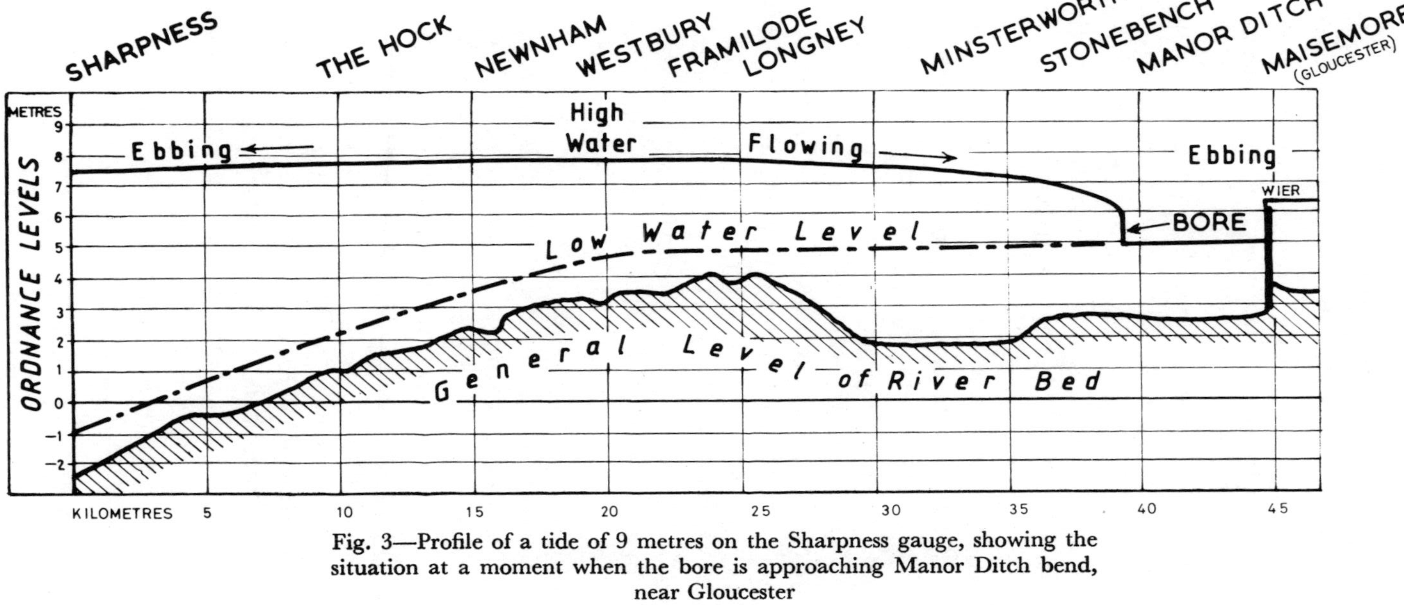

Fig. 3—Profile of a tide of 9 metres on the Sharpness gauge, showing the situation at a moment when the bore is approaching Manor Ditch bend, near Gloucester

tiny bore meets the 'weir', and practically a dead end. But it bounces back and runs away downstream as a wave of diminished size, just like the reflex bores that bounce back from the weirs at Gloucester.

Our model has demonstrated the physical features essential to bore formation and has made a bore in miniature before our very eyes. In the realm of modelling actual rivers, Sir Claude Inglis, late Director of the Hydraulics Research Station at Wallingford, made a reconstruction of Professor Gibson's original working tidal model of the River Severn to carry out further research into the 1945 Severn Barrage proposal. It was fascinating to watch the little bore behaving exactly as its full-size prototype.

When we have a mental picture of *how* a bore is formed there still remains a persistent 'Why?' It must be admitted at once that to the best of my belief the matter cannot be reduced to a *precise* mathematical formula fitting all cases. In view of the vast number of variables I think it may well have been carried as far as it possibly can be. A good deal of practical and theoretical research has been carried out, notably on the Trent in 1928 by H. N. Champion, and by the Director and Staff of the Liverpool Observatory and Tidal Institute, now the Institute of Oceanographic Sciences.

This chapter, like the rest of the book, is not designed as a scientific treatise, but simply to open the door a little to the ordinary enquirer. Nevertheless, to those with a knowledge of hydraulics who have not let their mathematics fall below Matriculation standard, I most strongly recommend a study of the exposition and calculations of the theory of bores by Doodson and Warburg, published for the first time in the *Admiralty Manual of Tides* in 1941. To reproduce these or anything like them here would be outside the intended scope of this book and a flagrant copy of other men's work, but I feel compelled to offer one quotation:

'. . . Hence a steep rise and a narrow entrance to a channel tend to give the same result, and if the conditions are favourable as regards depth so that the critical relations can be quickly obtained, a discontinuity in profile will result, and a bore will be formed. It must be realised, however, that as such critical conditions are approached the conditions on which the formulæ have been obtained are largely violated so that the formulæ cannot be used with great precision. They can only indicate the possibilities. As the critical value is approached, instability sets in, and the wave motion associated with the bore follows as a necessity of this.'

Before we can find, in simpler fashion, our own answer to the problem, three things must be understood. First, that every tide of the sea is a wave—a moving wave not very high but many miles in length, the length of a wave being the distance between two successive crests (Fig. 4).

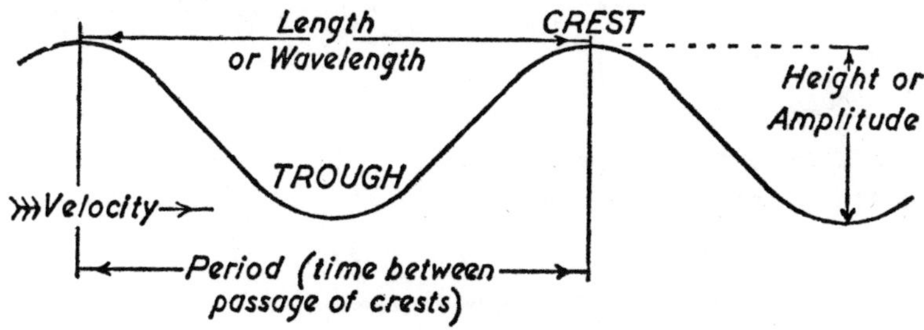

Fig. 4—General dimensions of any form of wave

The ordinary observer does not see tides as waves. At the sea-side we see the tide 'come in' as the water rises, and 'go out' as it falls, and may not realise we are watching a giant wave passing our point of observation. High water denotes the transit of the crest and low water the trough before the next great wave approaches. We can note the local height of the tide-wave against a pier or quay, but we cannot see its length. Yet in terms of time we perceive it to be just over twelve hours long, for that is the period between two successive high waters or successive low waters—the time it takes each complete tide-wave to pass by. However, the essential thing for our immediate purpose is to understand that every tide is a wave, and to think of it as such.

Next we must bear in mind that waves undergo changes in shape and speed when they run into shallower water, when the normal agitation of their particles is restricted by being near the bed. We will call this effect 'drag', and the resulting

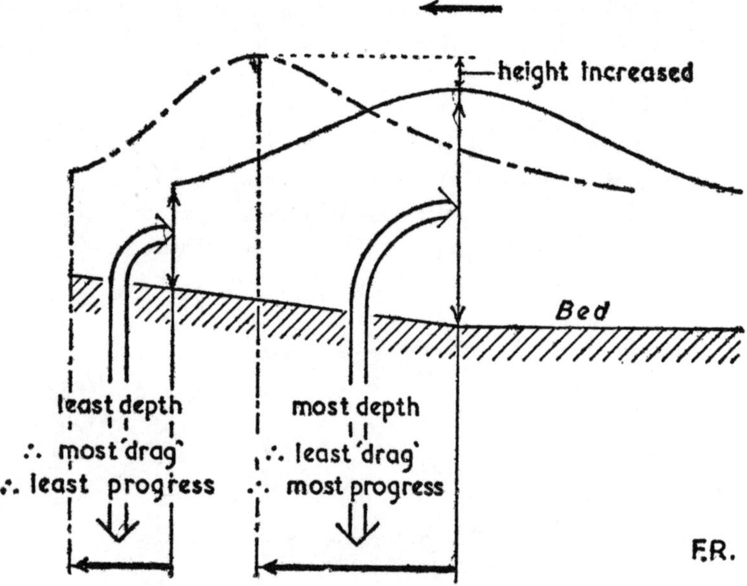

Fig. 5—How and why the tide wave is distorted by the rising bed of the estuary, as shown in Fig. 6

distortion of the tide-wave is illustrated in Fig. 5. The third factor is that friction between water and its containing channel has a considerable effect on the movement of the water. Wherever water is in contact with bed or banks it is slowed down by friction, and this retarding extends with gradually diminishing effect right into the main body of water. While on the subject we may as well note that in a straight stream of regular section the maximum velocity is slightly below the surface in mid-stream normally, not at the very surface as might be expected.

THE COURSE AND CAUSES OF THE BORE

The true ocean tide, approaching Europe from the Atlantic, is but three to five feet high. About two hundred miles off-shore it runs rather suddenly into shallower water on the 'continental shelf'. The decrease in depth slows it down, with the result that, while its length is shortened, its height increases. The same sort of thing happens to ordinary wind waves approaching the sea-shore—some days you wonder where the waves on the beach come from, for they are imperceptible a little way out. They are being amplified by running into shallow water. So the tide-wave is first amplified by the continental shelf.

Soon a section of the tide finds itself trapped between two land masses—South Wales and the Cornish peninsula. As the land closes in, the wave must contract its width; its volume is accommodated by further increasing its height. Between Pembroke and Hartland Point the width or frontage of the wave is fifty miles. But in the next eighty-five miles up to Avonmouth this contracts to a bare five miles, hence the wave is 'squeezed up' to a great height as it enters the Severn estuary.

When a tide enters the shallowing waters of an estuary, two distinct types of motion occur, for the *movement of the tide-wave* gives rise to a *flowing of the water,* called the 'tidal stream'. The wave is affected by what we are calling 'drag', and the flowing water by true friction. Approaching the Severn estuary from the sea, the tide-wave has a 'natural' symmetrical form; its front and back slopes are alike and equal. The progressive diagrams in Fig. 6 show how the wave becomes distorted for the reason illustrated in Fig. 5. Owing to the upward slope of the bed of the estuary, the water is shallower at the front of the wave than at any other part. Therefore the main body of the wave moves more quickly than the front, which it tends to over-run. Consequently the front slope becomes steeper while the back slope flattens out. The crest of the wave is thrown forward rather like passengers in a bus when the driver brakes sharply.

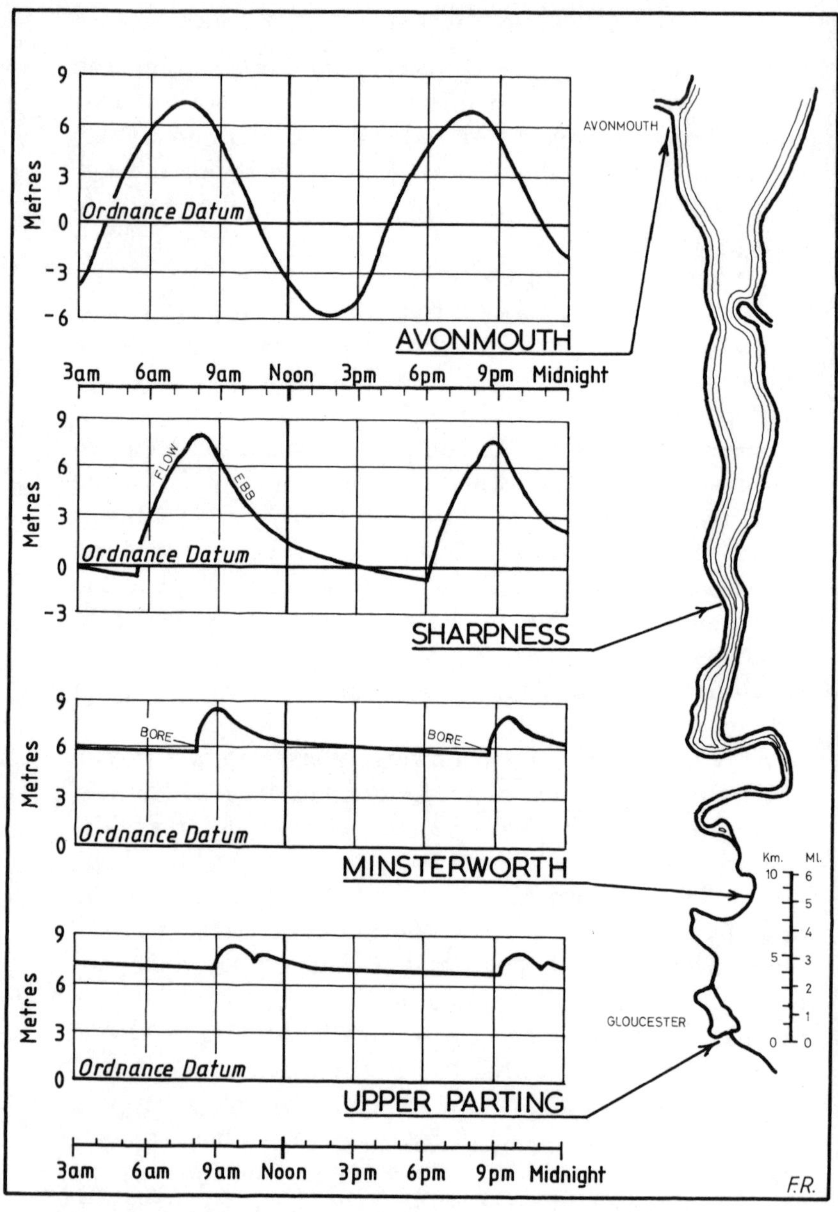

Fig. 6—Progressive water levels ('tide curves') taken throughout the rise and fall of two consecutive spring tides as they move up the river from Avonmouth to Gloucester. The distortion of the shape of the tide wave causes the bore to form

We can see much the same thing happen when an ordinary wind-caused wave runs up a sloping sea shore, but here the process is carried further until the front slope of the wave becomes so steep that it collapses. Then the whole wave breaks down, usually by the crest completely overtaking the toe and falling over as a 'plunging breaker'.

We can now list the principal factors, forces and influences whose nett outcome is the bore. First there is the height and velocity of the tide-wave and the depth of the water in which it runs; then there is the upward gradient of the estuary bed, against which the tide must overcome 'drag', friction and gravity, plus the normal downward flowing of the river. To these must be added the progressive constriction of the width of the tide-wave as the estuary narrows. Under this combination of conditions the toe of the front slope of the tide-wave can become sufficiently out of equilibrium to assume the special wave-form we know as a bore. When running 'free', bore waves have approximately the same shape or profile as wind waves—a form very nearly trochoidal (Fig. 7).

But are not the factors we listed common to all estuaries? Indeed they are. Why, then, do so few rivers have bores? It is all a matter of degree and of the relative proportions of the various factors. In the case of the Severn and other bore-forming rivers, the relative proportions are such as will bring about that critical condition in which the toe of the tide-wave develops a subsidiary wave system of its own. Bore waves are in a category of their own. You will observe in nature two general classifications of waves. There are those, like wind-waves, tide-waves and shock-waves, in which the shape moves on but the water does not. Then we have 'standing waves', such as you find at the foot of a weir or below sluice gates, in which the shape remains stationary but the water moves on. But in a large bore both the shape and the water are moving, though not at the same speed.

As regards breaking, bore waves obey the general rule of all waves and break if their height exceeds the depth of water in which they run. If the water shallows gently they break as 'spillers', but where the bed shelves sharply they break as 'plungers' (Fig. 7). Spillers are the waves of which surf is made. Wherever the river is deep enough, the bore runs smooth and unbroken except against the banks.

The manner in which the flow of the river is reversed when the bore passes is rather involved. With small bores the normal downward flow comes gently to a standstill after the

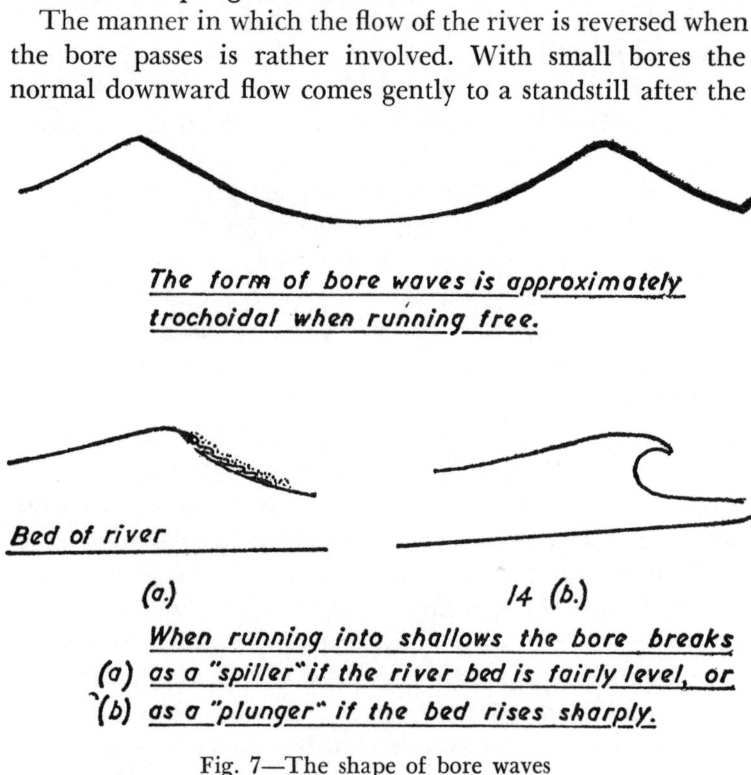

Fig. 7—The shape of bore waves

bore has gone by and it may be a minute before the upward stream gathers momentum. Even with the biggest bores the immediate reversal of the flow is only on the surface, the tide virtually running over the top of the normal stream. I have investigated in some detail the manner in which the change of direction comes about, with different tides and varying amounts of freshwater. Suffice it to say here that the general rule is for the reversal to work downwards from the surface to the bed. I have found the water near the bed still flowing downwards for up to ten minutes after the surface has been suddenly reversed by the passage of a fairly large bore.

To revert to the progress of the tide-wave up the estuary, as it approaches Minsterworth it leaves the wide tapering part of the 'funnel' and enters the 'stem'. The transition, of course, is nothing like so clearly defined as in a real funnel or in our model. Nevertheless, it takes place. Between Longney and the lower end of Minsterworth the narrowing process becomes less and less acute, and from Minsterworth to Gloucester the width is almost constant. A similar thing happens to the bed. The sharp rise eases off at Longney and, while having many ups and downs, the bed from Minsterworth to Gloucester has no over-all gradient at all.

So at Minsterworth, headed now by a well-formed bore, the tide-wave enters a channel of different character. No more dried-out sand-banks; no more narrowing of the tide-way; no more steep inclines and shallow rapids to be surmounted. Tides reach their maximum height above sea level (not to be confused with their maximum tidal range) at Framilode, which is just below Longney. This elevation of the tide water, acting like a hydrostatic head, pushes a mass of water—as much as will go—into the 'stem of the funnel' with enough energy to keep it going all the way to Tewkesbury and beyond. The main body of the great tide cannot enter the narrow 'stem', and begins to flow back to the sea, leaving its off-shoot to carry on alone as the 'projected' tide we mentioned earlier. That, at any rate, is one way of looking at it and as near the mark as one can get without being highly technical.

On rolls the bore towards Gloucester, revelling in its easier circumstances. Even so, it does not find the channel dead straight and perfectly regular throughout, so variations of its form are inevitable. It may subside a little, but will rise again; break, but gather again; swing to one side, and straighten up again—and so continue, apparently undiminished by any sapping of its energy, until it meets the great obstruction of the Gloucester weirs.

As in the case of tide-waves, the waves of the bore are affected by 'drag', so, since the depth of the river varies from place to place, it follows that bore heights are greatest where the depth only slightly exceeds the height of the wave—that is, where there is just sufficient water to prevent the wave breaking. The same factors cause the speed of the bore in this length to vary between ten and thirteen miles an hour. Thus the exact timing of the bore's arrival at any particular place is affected by the amount of freshwater in the river. The acceleration of the bore when freshwater is present is partially off-set, however, by the increased speed of the downward flow against which the bore must run.

The distortions of the great tide-wave, and the changes it undergoes between Avonmouth and Gloucester, are illustrated in Fig. 6, by graphs showing the rise and fall of a tide at four places on its journey. These graphs are called 'tide curves', and although the horizontal dimensions are in units of time rather than distance, they give some idea of the actual shape of the wave in a concertina'd form, the vertical scale being tremendously exaggerated.

At Avonmouth, which can be taken as the mouth of the Severn estuary and the beginning of the Bristol Channel, the curve is fairly symmetrical; the wave has not yet encountered all the distorting conditions of the estuary. The tidal range is very high. Indeed, a few miles upstream, off Beachley, the tidal range has been known to reach fifty feet; that is, fifty feet of vertical rise from low water to high. This is exceeded in only one other part of the world—in the Bay of Fundy, between Nova Scotia and New Brunswick, where it gives rise to the bore of the Petitcodiac river.

Incidentally, the great tidal range of the Severn near Beachley (or Aust) is not the only remarkable tidal feature of the river in that neighbourhood. I shall quite understand if you flatly refuse to believe me, but low water there falls lower than anywhere else, 'upstream, downstream, or in the Bristol

(4) *The bore approaches Lower Parting*

(5) *Around Manor Ditch bend is stonework 2 metres high*

(6) *Hurrying power*

(7) *Gliding, sweeping, crashing upstream*

Channel'. In case the significance of that is not at first apparent, let me put it another way. *Never,* under any circumstances, does the water upstream *or downstream* fall as low as it does in the Beachley to Avonmouth length (Fig. 8). But how can water possibly get out of a place and leave a hollow when the levels above and below are always higher?

It results from what is known as tidal resonance or 'standing oscillation', which occurs when certain bays and estuaries cause the tide to oscillate, or swing to and fro. In the Bristol Channel and lower part of the Severn estuary, the phenomenon can be likened to the way one sometimes sets the bathwater swaying from end to end of the bath; it behaves like a see-saw, leaping up at alternate ends, without changing level in the middle. That is resonance, the point in the middle being the 'node'. Once in motion, the swinging is very persistent and not easy to stop—as many wet bathroom floors could testify! As with a pendulum, only a tiny force, applied at each swing, is required to keep it going indefinitely.

Something like this happens in the Bristol Channel. Imagining Beachley to be one end of the bath, the receding tide swings like a pendulum towards the sea and the swaying motion is given a new impulse by each in-coming tide to keep it going. Tidal resonance plays some part in creating the high range in the Severn estuary, but the greater factor is the progressive narrowing of the Bristol Channel, coupled with the upward slope of its bed.

Having studied within our intended scope all that goes into the making of a bore it might be appropriate to sum up before concluding the chapter. Rather than do this in my own words, we may get a fresh angle if I quote some authoritative writings. The views expressed vary a little, but in all you will find something of what we have been discussing.

In 1837 John Scott Russell wrote, in a *Report of inquiries made by the Committee of the British Association*:

'A tidal bore is formed when the water is so shallow at low water that the first waves of the flood tide move with a velocity so much less than that due to the succeeding part of the tide wave, as to be overtaken by the subsequent waves, or wherever the tide rises so rapidly and the water on the shore or in the river is so shallow that the height of the first wave of the tide is greater than the depth of the fluid at that place.'

One only hopes the meaning of this long sentence is better understood here than it would have been at the beginning of the chapter!

Next in chronological order, Captain Beechey, R.N., F.R.S., who made a most famous *Survey of the River Severn* in 1849,

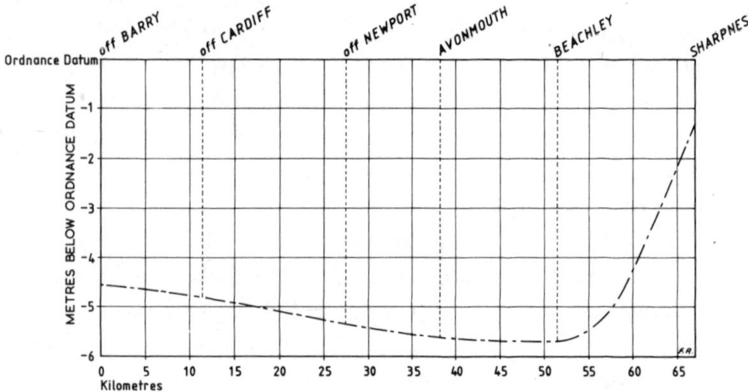

Fig. 8—Relative levels attained by low water in the lower estuary

used in his *Report* the expression 'The bore—or the foot of the wave' and stated:

'On a comparison of the rates of the tidal wave and the bore, it appears that, in the early stages of the tide, the crest of the tide wave is rapidly overtaking the bore, and, consequently, momentarily increasing the height of it; and there can be no doubt that this retardation of the foot of the wave, occasioned by friction of shallows and sand banks, is the primary cause of the bore.'

Nearer our own times, Herbert Chatley, D.Sc., M.I.C.E., F.R.A.S., wrote in his foreword to Russell and MacMillan's excellent book *Waves and Tides* (Hutchinson, 1952).

'Still another analogy occurs in the behaviour of breakers and bores. When the depth of water is roughly speaking the same as the height of the wave, the wave breaks. In the case of a bore the depth of water has a similar effect in starting the bore even though there is some difference mechanically.'

Finally a paragraph from the *Admiralty Navigation Manual,* Volume I:

'The natural slope of any wave is regular, but when a wave enters shallow water its front slope increases and its rear slope decreases in steepness. In rivers and estuaries, and in shallow water generally, the duration of the rise is therefore less than the duration of the fall. In rivers, the steepness of the front slope may be increased and the wave tends to break; should it break a bore occurs in which half or more of the total rise of the tide may occupy only a few minutes.'

So there we are! But still I think most of us will best comprehend the matter by thinking of the model demonstration, while he who is suitably equipped will find no better exposition of the theory and mathematics of bores than that of Doodson and Warburg in the *Admiralty Manual of Tides.*

Chapter 3

WHEN?

The sophisticated lady standing on the river bank, awaiting a little impatiently the arrival of the bore, turned and remarked to her escort, 'This bore thing only happens once a year, I suppose?' He said he 'thought so'. I could not help wondering how many more of the hundreds who lined the Severn banks on that rather chilly morning thought so too. For the idea that the bore can be seen but once or twice a year is widely held. Even in places no more than five miles from the bore's domain one still meets those who believe the bore to be a once-a-year affair. The more learned of them will tell you it happens on Good Friday.

There are reasons why such a belief came into being. First, there can be a bore on Good Friday, of course, and it may be a big one, because Good Friday falls near the vernal equinox, when tides run high. Next we must bear in mind that until not so many years ago days off work were few and far between for most people. Good Friday was the only holiday near an equinox, so if folk spent it by the river and a bore happened on that day it was the only one they ever saw. Furthermore, although it amounts to nothing, there is the suggestion of an astronomical relationship between the date of Good Friday and the occurrence of the bore. In the days I am speaking of village churches were well attended and during the interminable sermons people were prone to do as I did and thumb through the preliminary pages of the Prayer Book, where we learned that Easter Day (on which the date of Good Friday

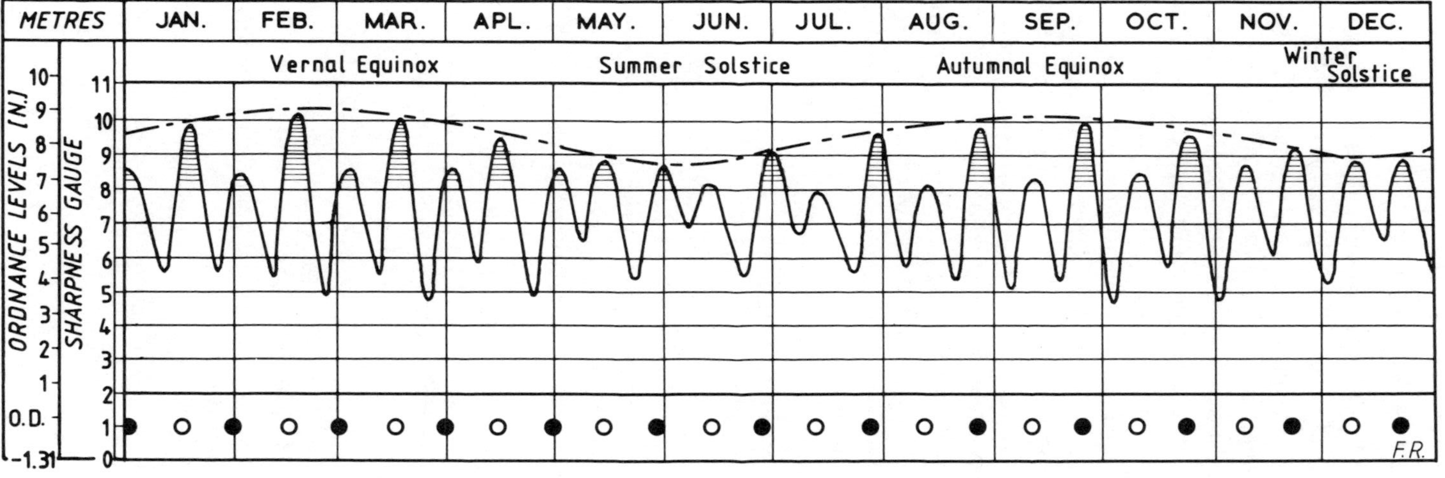

Fig. 9—Graph showing how the heights of tides at Sharpness vary throughout a typical year, following the phases of the moon. The humps and dips are periods of spring tides and neap tides respectively. Note the fortnightly, monthly and seasonal cycles of changes, and how the major and minor spring-tide periods of each lunar month change order in the summer solstice and revert back in the winter. Not only are spring tides higher in the equinoxial seasons, but the neaps are lower. Under normal river conditions all tides in the shaded portions of the lumps are bore tides

depends) 'is always the first Sunday after the Full Moon which happens upon or next after the Twenty-first day of March'. This tittle of information, together with the knowledge that the full moon has something to do with big tides, and big tides with bores, would be quite sufficient to settle the matter in the minds of those who knew no other bore than the one they saw on a Good Friday. But the ecclesiastical full moon does not occur on the same day as the astronomical full moon.

The plain fact is that there are between 250 and 260 bores every year, counting the big ones and medium ones together. This means two a day on about 130 days of the year, though the number varies somewhat. A further 150 tides a year cause the level of the river to heave suddenly in the form of a long smooth wave, washing a little at the banks but hardly discernible in mid-stream. The flow does not reverse immediately and we do not call this swell a bore, though it is a baby one and gives the impression that the river is bewitched.

However, our main interest is in proper bores, numbering, as I have said, between 250 and 260 per annum. They do not roll up with monotonous regularity, nor yet haphazard. The sequence of their occurrence and the variation of their sizes accord with a wonderful system of cycles within cycles. Fig. 9 shows as a graph the changes in the heights of tides over a whole year, while one month's twice-daily tides are detailed in Fig. 10.

The days on which bores occur come in groups of three, four, or up to seven days at a time. The interval between the middle day of one group and the middle day of the next is a fortnight, or half a lunar month. In each group the size of the bore grows from a small one on the first day to a maximum on the middle day then declines. Seven days after the maximum there is no vestige of tide where the bore was wont to run. Yet another seven days and we are in the middle of the next group. But I deceive you a little about the seven days; seven days to the hour would be too good to be true. The period is a little longer by just a few hours. Although the lunar month

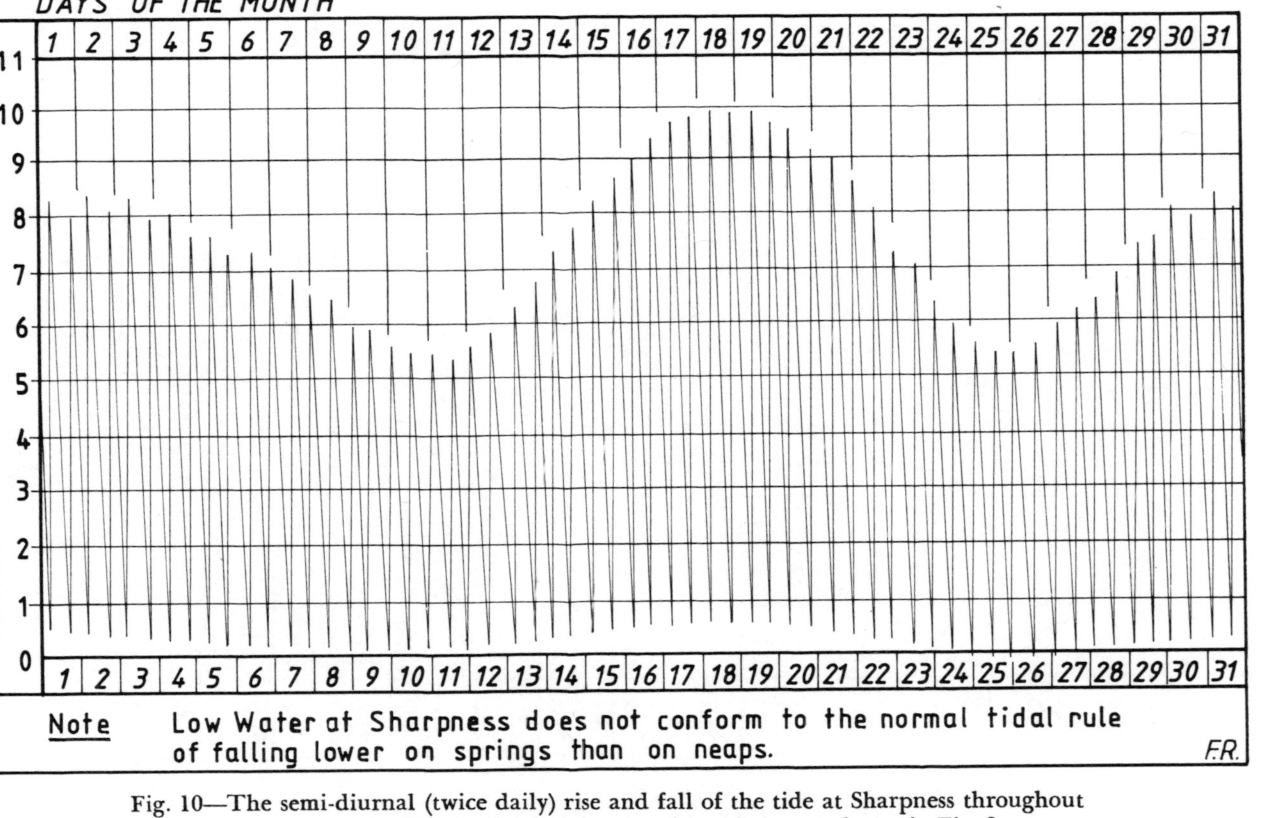

Fig. 10—The semi-diurnal (twice daily) rise and fall of the tide at Sharpness throughout a typical month. The levels of high water form the curve shown in Fig. 9

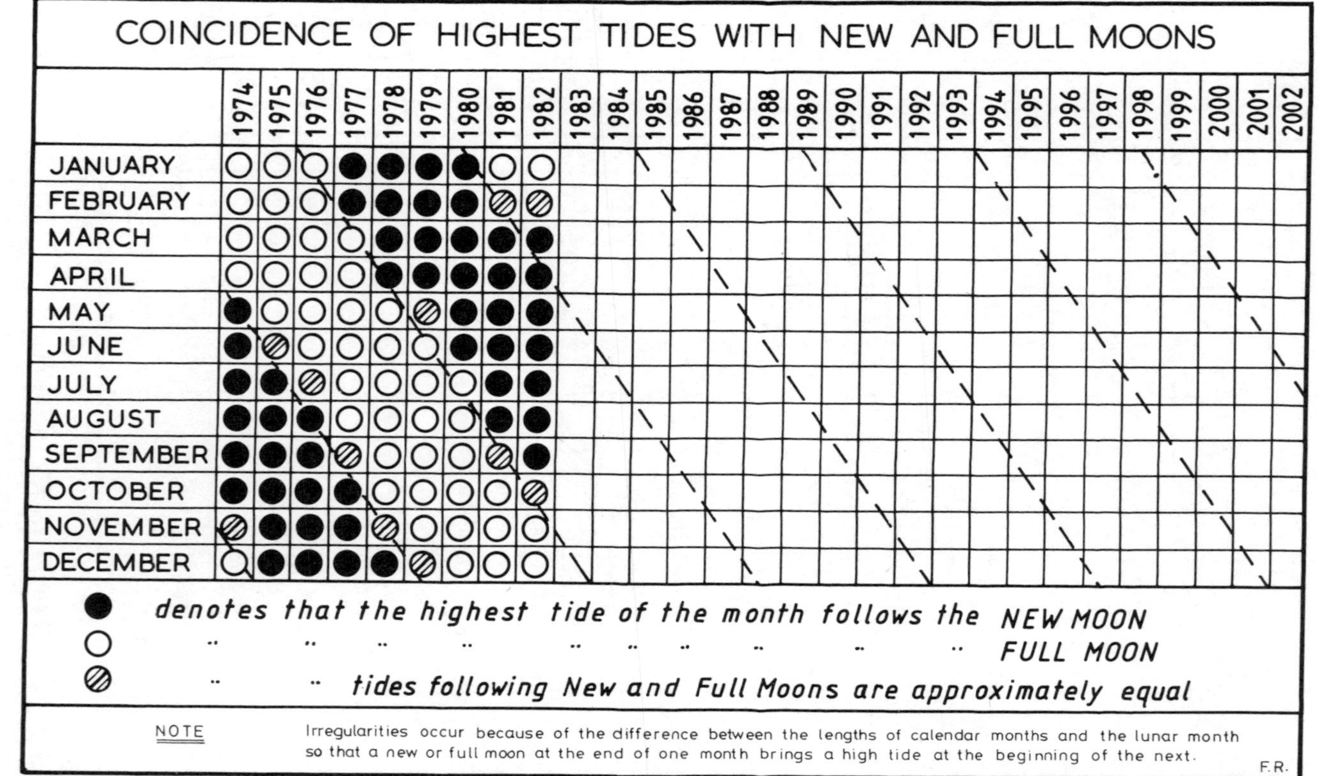

Fig. 11—Moons and high tides

consists of four of these 'seven day' periods—two with bores and two without—and although the lunar month of common usage is 28 days, the true lunar month is 29 days, 12 hours, 44 minutes—the average time it takes the moon to encircle the moving earth. The groups of 'bore days' march with the phases of the moon, but the rhythm is slightly syncopated, for maximum bores do not coincide exactly with new and full moons, but arrive one to three days later.

There are many who think the highest tides—hence the biggest bores—come at the time of the full moon; others think they come with the new moon. Both beliefs are half true—at least, each is true half the time. Like almost everything to do with tides, it is a matter of cycles. For nearly seven consecutive months the biggest tides come with the new moon, then for a similar period with the full, then back again, completing the cycle of the year every nine years. You will see how it goes by studying Fig. 11, in which I have set out the sequence for nine years. Incidentally, besides showing how the changes progress, the chart enables you to do a little prediction of your own. Beyond 1982 the 'moons' have not been filled in, but the pattern-lines have been extended and you can fill in the 'moons' yourself for several years ahead, or can tell at a glance that, for example, the highest tide of March 1988 will occur with a new moon, so we shall not plan to see that one by moonlight. Let it be quite clear, nevertheless, that when the new moon brings the highest tide of a month, there is quite a fair tide with the full moon too; and *vice versa*.

I suppose one may safely assume that the great majority of people are interested chiefly, if not exclusively, in the big bores—those likely to be spectacular. That narrows down the number attracting attention to not more than fifty a year, of which half will be in the evening, though not necessarily in the dark. The seasons, too, become restricted to two quarters: February-March-April and August-September-October.

Here I would add what may amount to yet another restriction. It concerns principally those who have never seen a bore, or have seen but few. One's reaction on seeing the bore for the first time depends a great deal on what one expects to see. For instance, some years ago a national daily newspaper made the staggering announcement that on such and such a day 'a wall of water thirty feet high will roll up the Severn', so if anyone believed such nonsense (which arose from there being a 30 ft tide on the Sharpness gauge) they would have been terribly disappointed in the bore that actually came, although it was quite a good one. On the other hand, some tourists who had stopped to picnic by the river at Minsterworth and had never (so they told me afterwards) so much as heard of the bore, were tremendously thrilled when a small one came along unheralded. I have known two people see their first bore together and one be overawed while the other is unimpressed. Experience indicates that most depends on what one expects to see.

Writers in the age of more florid styles produced some graphic descriptions of the bore. Thomas Harral, for example, wrote in 1824 'When the Boar comes, the stream does not swell by degrees, as at other times, but rolls in with a head . . . foaming and roaring as though it were enraged by the opposition which it encounters.' Elsewhere he states 'Turbulence, foam, dashing, and noise then accompany the rolling of an inconceivable body of water, which, rising mountain high, excites the most terrific ideas.' So it would seem! And he continues 'Such is the force of the current at the equinoxes that it sometimes rushes with uncontrollable fury twenty or thirty miles up the country, inundating the low lands to a vast extent. Occasionally, the rapidity is so great, that the tide rises several feet in a minute, foaming and raging like a hideous whirlpool.' Somewhat earlier, Rudder had stated 'So dreadful is the devastating progress of the Boar, that they who are overtaken by it on the river's bank are inevitably lost.'

The facts stated by these writers are substantially true, yet are so expressed as to convey, I think, to the twentieth century reader an exaggerated impression of the bore. The script and illustrations of this book are most carefully designed therefore to give only a true and fair impression. The heights of bores illustrated can be gauged from the fact that the river banks are twelve to fourteen feet high.

Perhaps I should give warning that the bore can be temperamental. When mentioning the incidence of the bore I have used the expression 'may be expected' rather than 'will occur'. This is done very deliberately because no long-range forecast can give the slightest guarantee that a particular high tide will, in fact, be the occasion of a spectacular bore. Sometimes the bore of a quite exceptionally high tide is nothing phenomenal.

The capriciousness of the bore is rather amusing—to river people at least. You can hardly be expected to appreciate this if you suffer disappointment after journeying miles to see the thing, but it seems to show an occasional dislike for playing to the gallery. I have seen it treat with disdain an audience of thousands, gliding languidly by with an air of contempt like a coy madam slighting her admirers. Its 'party piece' performance is well nigh unpredictable; it may be up to average, it may be shy and sulky, or it may positively show off. Every now and then, when no exceptional tide is predicted and none but the river's own people are there to see, the bore will come crashing along with a terrific head, hurling itself clean out of the banks.

On the whole, though, its behaviour is fairly rational, considering what a lot of things there are to upset it, and we on the spot can usually tell a day or two beforehand whether it will be up to standard. But no one can say months ahead; hence this caution. In any event, the fair-minded visitor is wise enough to appreciate that to see one isolated bore, at one particular part of its long journey, will hardly justify a sweeping claim to 'know what the bore is like'. One does not see all who sees but one.

Now we ask 'How can we discover for ourselves the date

when a big bore is likely?' and on reflection we find the answer has been embodied in preceding pages. It can be done by anybody, quickly and simply, without resorting to tide-tables or to any out-of-the-way source of special information.

To start with, we know the date will be near an equinox, in March or September or their flanking months. To find the actual day of the month, refer first to Fig. 11 and see whether the maximum tide of the month in which you are interested comes with the new moon or the full. Then take your diary or almanac or anything giving the dates of the moon's phases, and look up the date in your chosen month of the full or new moon, whichever the table indicated as giving the maximum tide. Two days after that date, if other conditions are not unfavourable, there will be, quite definitely, a large bore. Frequently it will be the biggest of its group. In any event it will be very nearly so, for you cannot be more than one day out, either before or after.

Obviously, the most direct means of finding exact dates is to look up the maximum tides in a Bristol Channel *Tide Table* for the current year. Should you wish to obtain one a booklet containing full tables for all Bristol Channel ports, together with a lot of other navigational information, is published annually by J. W. Arrowsmith Ltd., of Bristol. Alternatively Arrowsmith's '*Bristol and Channel Ports Tide Table* (*Short*)' may be obtained from booksellers. This includes the Sharpness tables and is all one needs for full predictions of bores. There is no simple 'constant' accurately linking Sharpness times with those for Dover or London Bridge.

But because every tide embraces all our shores, it follows that on days when the Bristol Channel has high tides, so do all other places. Therefore the tide table for any place round our coast will indicate when a bore is likely. Most public libraries have tide tables. They may be separate tables for a local place, or complete sets for many ports arranged together in a nautical almanac.

Having gained access to a current year's tide tables for any

BLUNTNESS DOCK

	Time	Metres
1 Tu	0207	5·2
	1014	–0·3
	1442	5·3
	2309	–0·2
2 W	0338	5·1
	1155	–0·3
	1614	5·8
3 Th	0052	–0·2
	0458	6·1
	1329	–0·3
	1723	6·6
4 F	0214	–0·1
	0555	6·8
	1443	–0·1
	1811	7·4
5 Sa	0312	–0·1
	0639	7·6
	1534	–0·1
	1848	7·6
6 Su	0354	–0·1
	0711	7·8
	1608	–0·1
	1922	8·1
7 M	0430	0·0
	0746	8·3
	1641	0·0
	1955	8·2
8 Tu	0459	0·0
	0818	8·3
	1710	0·0
	2026	8·2
9 W	0527	0·0
	0845	8·6
	1735	0·0
	2055	8·4
10 Th	0553	0·0
	0914	8·5
	1806	0·0
	2123	8·3

Fig. 12—A typical Tide Table arrangement giving high and low water

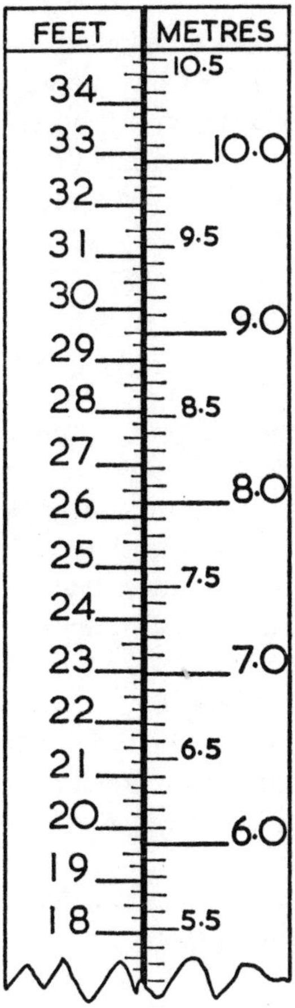

Tide Tables and Tide Gauges were metricated as from 1 January 1972. The old style Sharpness gauge is compared here with the new.

of our ports all you have to do is to scan the 'heights' columns, find the highest tide, and note the date. If you are using the table for any Bristol Channel port you now have the exact date when the biggest bore may be expected. The tables for certain other ports may be one day out, either for local reasons or simply because each tide takes a day to travel round the coasts of Britain.

A word about reading tide tables may be helpful. A typical arrangement is shown in Fig. 12. The hours are normally expressed in the 24-hour system, in which case times up to 12.59 (nearly one o'clock middle day) are read as printed, but if you want to convert the rest of the day's times into common usage you naturally subtract 12 hours from each. There are minor variations in the mode of printing the 24-hour system, but usually the time column is clearly headed to indicate hours and minutes, often as four consecutive unpunctuated digits as in Fig. 12. All times are in Greenwich Mean Time (G.M.T.) so an hour has to be added during British Summer Time.

You will come across occasional blanks where a tide appears to have been missed out. But when you recall that the average interval between successive high waters is 12 hrs. 25 mins. you will realise that when a morning high water is but a few minutes before midday, the next high water will be just after midnight, not in the evening of the day in question. It will be the next day's morning tide. Hence the blank.

There remains one more way of finding the date when a big bore may be expected. The old song said 'If you want to know the time, ask a policeman', and I would not put it beyond many a local 'bobby' to tell you the date of the next bore, if not the time of it as well! Almost certainly he could direct you to someone who can supply the answer. But he has much else to do, so I will direct you myself. Enquire of any of the following who can tell you not only the date, but the time of high water at Sharpness:

Severn Trent Water Authority,
River Section (South),
124 London Road,
Gloucester, GL1 3PL — Telephone: Gloucester 29847

or Severn Trent Water Authority,
Southwick Park,
Gloucester Road,
Tewkesbury, Glos. GL20 7DG — Telephone: Tewkesbury 294516

Both the above issue bore schedules for the whole year upon request. These are also published in local newspapers at about the turn of the year. Information may also be obtained from:

British Waterways Board,
Dock Office,
Gloucester, GL1 2EJ — Telephone: Gloucester 25524

or their Sharpness Office — Telephone: Dursley 811644

or the Gloucester newspaper:
The Citizen,
St. John's Lane,
Gloucester, GL1 2AY — Telephone: Gloucester 424442

Having then, by one means or another, found the date we sought, it remains to find the time at which we should turn up to see the bore on that day. All bores worth seeing occur between 7 a.m. and noon, and 7 p.m. and midnight. So we can say for certain that our visit will have to be either in the morning or evening; not in the afternoon. Beyond that we cannot go without resort to tide tables, for there is no simple rule-of-thumb method such as I gave for finding the date. Bore times are related to the times of high water at Sharpness, but the time at which we shall see the bore depends also on where we shall see it, so that is the next thing to decide. The next chapter will help you choose a suitable place, and with that settled and having ascertained the time of high water at Sharpness on the day in question, the following table, or Fig. 13, will tell you how many minutes to add or subtract from the time of high water at Sharpness to find the approximate time the bore may be expected to pass the place of your choosing. For reasons explained elsewhere the bore's arrival can be up to twenty minutes later than the calculated moment, but it is not likely to be earlier. Nevertheless, always allow plenty of time; better to wait half an hour than miss the bore by seconds.

TIME OF THE BORE AT PRINCIPAL VIEW POINTS

Before or after High Water at Sharpness under average conditions

Maisemore Bridge	add 40 mins.
Over Bridge	add 35 mins.
Lower Parting	add 33 mins.
Manor Ditch Bend	add 27 mins.
Upper Rea, Hempsted	add 20 mins.
Stonebench	add 15 mins.
Elmore Back Minsterworth Ferry	high water at Sharpness
The Denny, Minsterworth	subtract 3 mins.
Severn Bore Inn	subtract 7 mins.
Waterend	subtract 10 mins.
Epney	subtract 20 mins.
Framilode	subtract 25 mins.
Westbury Strand	subtract 45 mins.
Broadoak	subtract 50 mins.
Newnham	subtract 60 mins.
Bullo Pill	subtract 67 mins.
Overton	subtract 78 mins.
The Hock	subtract 85 mins.
Haywards Point, Awre	subtract 90 mins.

Chapter 4

WHERE TO SEE THE BORE

As a spectacle, the bore is worth seeing only between the limits of Overton near Fretherne and Maisemore near Gloucester, and within this length is generally at its best between Minsterworth and Lower Parting, Gloucester. Nevertheless, a good wave of somewhat different character may be seen between Overton and Minsterworth. Fig. 13 shows most of the reasonably accessible viewing points, also local roads and by-ways connecting with main roads from further afield.

Without a doubt the best known place for seeing the bore is STONEBENCH on the east side of the river three and a half miles by road from Gloucester Cross. Best known, perhaps; but a place to be avoided, I think, when the highest bores are due and the lanes become choked with hopeful viewers. Stonebench is not a village. One would hardly be justified in calling it even a hamlet, though its largest house was once an inn.

A 'bench', in river parlance, means a shelf of rock in the bed of the river. Such a bench exists here, extending three-quarters of the way across the river from the very point where road and river part company. Without making any geological distinctions, it is a stone bench. This descriptive designation became its proper name, and in due course widened its application to embrace the adjacent land on the left bank; which reminds me to mention that standard practice is to speak of river banks as 'right' or 'left' as one would see them from mid-river when looking in a *downstream* direction.

The inn owed its origin to the rock, for in past days, when the river was regularly navigated, the bench was a barrier trading vessels could not pass at low water. They had to tie up and wait anything from a few hours to a week or more, until the next tide or a spate of freshwater gave them sufficient depth to pass over. And who would begrudge their hard-working crews a little hospitality in the meantime, and a brief respite from the dank and dark discomfort of the wretched accommodation aboard their trows? Throughout all the navigated length of the Severn you find waterside inns of similar origin. They mark the shallows where Severn sailors of a bygone age had to 'wait for water'.

Stonebench's reputation as a grandstand for viewing the bore was well founded, for here were combined the two essentials; the constricted width of the river amplified the bore, while the road provided easy access and good riverside standing space. But conditions have changed and the bore is no longer any more spectacular at Stonebench than elsewhere because in the mid-1930s the late Severn Catchment Board improved the channel all the way from Minsterworth up to Gloucester, removing the Stonebench constriction and providing a standard width throughout.

On the western bank the counterpart of Stonebench is MINSTERWORTH where road congestion can never be so bad as in the Stonebench lanes. The main road skirts the river almost continuously for nearly two miles and traffic is soon away when the bore has passed. There is direct access to the river bank at the Severn Bore Inn, the Denny, near the old Ferry or at the Church at the upstream end of the village. Or you can get away from the crowds by walking along the flood-bank as far as you like towards Gloucester; it is a public footpath all the way. With a car, the bore can be overtaken and seen at three or four different places without the slightest need to hurry or run risks. Go first to NEWNHAM, where a car park juts out into the river at the Gloucester end of the town.

When the bore has passed, drive in the direction of Gloucester until you reach one of the four named places at Minsterworth. Unless there are great crowds, you should be able to park comfortably. You have plenty of time in hand. After seeing the bore you again have ample time to move on towards Gloucester, where although parking is not practicable near the modern bridges at OVER and Telford's bridge is accessible only on foot, things are not so difficult a mile further on in the vicinity of MAISEMORE BRIDGE.

An additional feature can often be observed from Maisemore Bridge or that locality. If you wait about ten minutes after the bore has passed and keep an eye on the swift upflowing stream, against the banks in particular, you can see a distinct wave come slowly back against the racing water. It may be as much as a foot high, and is a reflex wave thrown back from the bore's encounter with Maisemore weir, a quarter of a mile upstream.

Telford's disused bridge at OVER is an easy walk from Gloucester, but the view of the bore as it gets near is obscured by the railway bridge. So why not go down to the river bank? The way is easy to find. Better still, get as far as possible from the noise of the road and railway by walking beside the river to LOWER PARTING or beyond. The bore is bigger below the Parting. A mile and a quarter from Over Bridge is the acute bend at MANOR DITCH, where the bore throws itself round the stone-lined bank.

Another fairly short walk from Gloucester is to the left bank at Lower Parting. Take either of the roads which lead past the Docks towards Hempsted. Just past the ruined portal of Llanthony Abbey turn into Sudmeadow Road, which will lead you straight down to Lower Parting, or from which you can take a path to the right and reach the Parting by walking down the left bank of the East Channel.

If you arrive at Lower Parting in plenty of time you may care to walk down the Severn bank to meet the bore. Naturally, by keeping near the riverside you cannot miss it. A mile brings you to the sharp bend opposite Manor Ditch, and if you want to make a circuit of the Hempsted peninsula, there is a fine straight mile down to UPPER REA, from where you can return by road through Hempsted village. At any point on this riverside walk, which is within such easy reach of the town, the bore can be seen to good advantage. Many of the photographs reproduced in this book were taken in this length. You get well away from crowds and into something approaching solitude. Here, utterly alone, I have seen a splendid bore when chaos has reigned at Stonebench, and Minsterworth was crowded.

If you have transport and do not want to walk many yards, the best place near Gloucester is Upper Rea, where you can drive to within a hundred paces of the river down the rather narrow lane out of Hempsted village. Parking space is not too plentiful, but room can be found even if it means a little further to walk. Having parked, and left free passage for others on the road, you reach the river by crossing a short plank bridge spanning a ditch, then making for the floodbank almost straight ahead. You go nowhere near the houses.

The next accessible place down the left bank is LOWER REA, which is where you first see the river on your direct way from Gloucester to Stonebench. You can see the bore here, but there is little room for parking, and my advice is to avoid it if big crowds are about; and if they are not, you might just as well go on another half mile to Stonebench itself.

A quarter of a mile below Stonebench is WEIR GREEN. It can be reached by road by a cul-de-sac off the road from Stonebench and Elmore. An increasing number of people who know the way go there to avoid the Stonebench crowds, but I have not seen the place unduly packed. Weir Green is another point from which you can set out on a nice walk downstream to meet the bore in solitude—or comparative solitude, depending on how far you go. You can follow the bank of the river past Windmill hill down to the bend at Madam Pool, then on to the hamlet of ELMORE BACK, opposite Minsterworth church and ferry—just about two miles in all. If you go all the way to Elmore Back it will still be shorter to return the way you came than to take the road.

Elmore Back can be reached, of course, without walking at all. In fact, those unable or unwilling to take many paces could find it admirable. Arriving at the riverside lane you can turn left or right and find viewing points either way. Turning right takes you to a point where the bore runs very high along the western bank; or by turning left you go hardly any distance before an obvious place presents itself.

With regard to finding the more remote riverside places, the system of lanes and byways is a regular maze and you may well find yourself retracing the very road you came down a quarter of an hour ago—and never know where you went wrong. So here, perhaps more than anywhere, must be observed the golden rule of bore viewing—'Allow plenty of time!'

There is nowhere on the eastern bank downstream of Elmore Back to see conveniently what we may call the 'river' bore. Soon the characteristics of a sandy estuary appear, and at the next place of easy access mud banks show in the tideway at low water, so the bore does not always span the river from side to side as it does upstream of the Severn Bore Inn at Minsterworth. A good bore, nevertheless, can be seen at WATEREND, washing the steep bank as it rounds the bend opposite Rosemary Point before straightening up for Minsterworth. You reach Waterend down a cul-de-sac lane turning off the road from Elmore to Longney at the appropriate signpost, on whose solitary arm 'Waterend' shares a place with 'Hayes End'.

If you do not take the turning to Waterend you arrive at LONGNEY, where you find a road junction with two completely opposite roads both signposted as leading to Gloucester—and quite truthfully, too. This is but a part of the maze of which I gave warning. LONGNEY CRIB, with its row of humble cottages, is not far away. Here we see to our right the wide expanse of Longney Sands, with Bush Crib just upstream on the same shore. To our left we look down the curving river to Framilode, with Epney in the middle distance. The deep water channel hugs the outside of the bend, and up this channel comes the bore, rising high against the bank with many a splash. Its right flank streams out over Rodley sands as a creaming wave when the river is very low; otherwise the head spans right across. But stand clear when 'flood's head' strikes the Crib!

We can walk down the river bank from Longney Crib in a few minutes to EPNEY, with its barge-made breakwater which is another of the bore's favourite splashing points. Close by is the Anchor inn, a centre of the local elvering industry. If you travel from Gloucester direct to Epney, you will save many miles of winding lanes by keeping to the A.38 Bristol road as far as Parkend, near Moreton Valence.

Leaving Epney for UPPER FRAMILODE the riverside road, hitherto often impassible at high water, is now protected from tidal flooding by a concrete wall. The church at Upper Framilode stands nearer to the water's edge than any other on the Severn. Very high tides used to reach to the doorstep before the concrete floodbank was built in 1961. Nearby, and side by side, are the mouth of the River Frome and the derelict entrance lock to the old Stroudwater Canal, through which Thames-bound vessels once left the Severn and boats from London reached the Severn tide.

Both Upper and Lower Framilode command wonderful views of the estuary, winding broadly away downstream (nevertheless in a north-westerly direction just here) towards the beautiful wooded hills of the Forest of Dean, where the sun goes down in summer time with a glory we shall not forget. The practised eye distinguishes an approaching bore a mile or more away as a thin white line creeping almost imperceptibly over the far-off sand banks, with occasional bursts of spray along the Pridings shore. Framilode marks the commencement of the Great Horseshoe Bend, holding in its arms the peninsula of Arlingham. Corresponding to Framilode's position on the upper arm (or is it a leg?) the lower limb of the Horseshoe ends at the Hock, barely a mile overland across the isthmus but nearly nine by river.

I remember standing in the silence of a moonlit night on the river bank at Framilode. A quiet air breathed from the south-west so softly that never a tree sighed in its sleep, when borne across the isthmus came a sound as of great seas breaking on a distant shore—and I knew the bore had reached the Hock. Yet soon it was again far out of earshot, rolling away westwards on its journey round the mighty bend. Stillness descended, and a whole hour would pass before I should glimpse, gleaming in the moonlight, that familiar line of whiteness over the sands off Pridings Point, and hear again the one sound that only the bore, the distant sea and a far-off train can make.

At the very apex of the Horseshoe bend ARLINGHAM PASSAGE faces Newnham across a quarter mile of tideway and if ever two places were opposite—in every shade of meaning—these are. Arlingham warth is low, flat and desolate, its foreshore a bank of mud, while Newnham's coloured cliff, endraped in greenery, lifts from the water to hold aloft the lovely church and spire, clustered about with all the roof-tops of this small historic town, whence Henry II in 1171 sailed on his expedition to Ireland. If you would hear the bells across the water, or the chimes or carillon, go to Arlingham Passage. But this is not the best of places for viewing the bore; nevertheless, it can be seen and the rapid inundation of the sands is quite remarkable.

The way down to Arlingham from the main Bristol road passes Fretherne church, with its much crocketed spire and pinnacles. Five hundred yards before reaching it, a field gate and stile on the left give access to a walk over two fields to the Severn bank, arriving near the muddy creek of HOCK DITCH. Away on the right rises the grey face of HOCK CLIFF, from whose stony beach flat shelves of rock stretch far

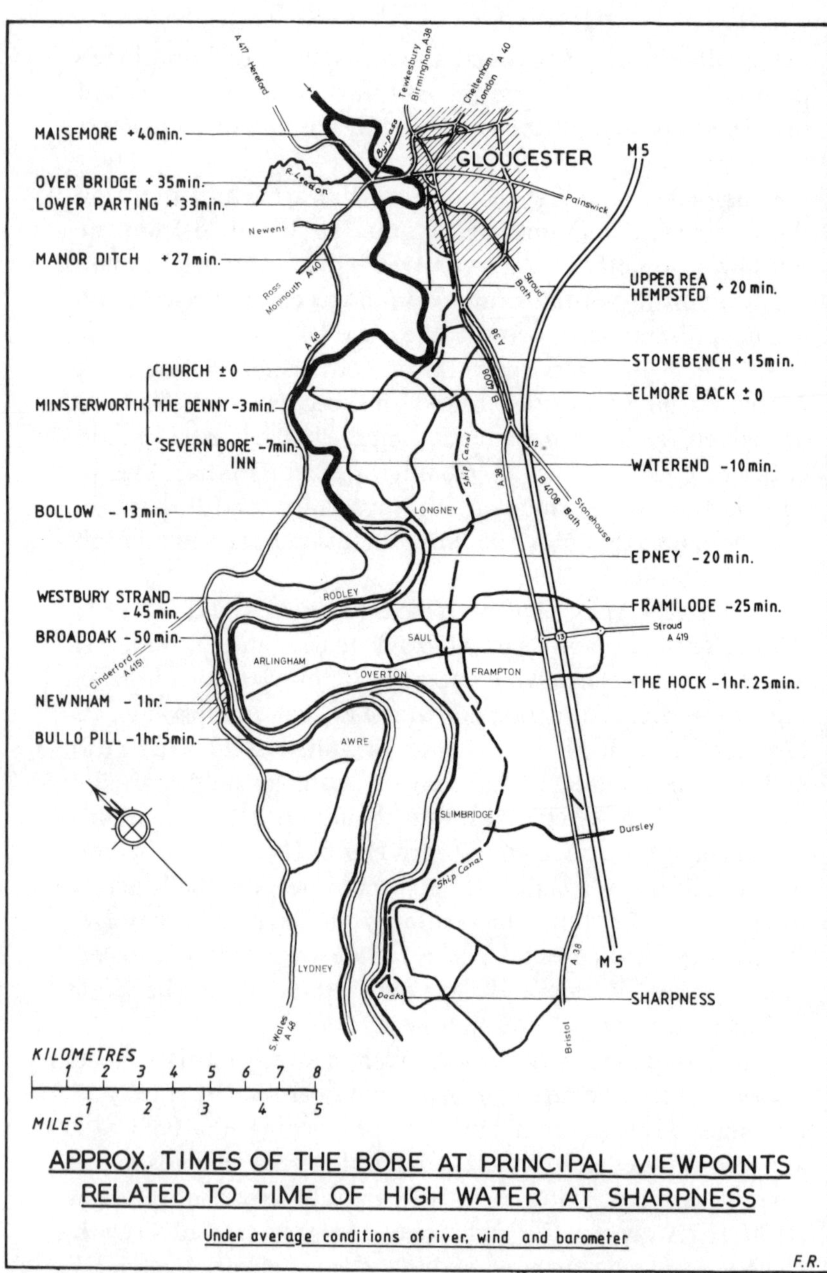

Fig. 13—Times of the bore at the principal viewpoints

out at low water and among which were the remnants of a massive masonry structure of some antiquity, the great breakwater known as Hock Crib.

At low water one can walk along the beach at the foot of Hock Cliff to reach OVERTON at its upstream end, but certainly not when a bore is due. I do not altogether recommend either Overton or the Hock as a place for one's very first visit to see the bore, but everyone should certainly 'see tide' at the Hock sometime or another. Even a small one is a sight to see.

Of BULLO and AWRE, both on the west side of the estuary, I would prefer Bullo, where the Pill was converted into a little dock for the export of Forest coal. At both places the rushing of the tide as it covers the sands is most impressive.

At NEWNHAM one may stand in the churchyard on the highest part of the cliff and see a panorama of the Horseshoe Bend, keeping the bore in view for three or four miles. In contrast a close-up is obtained from the water's edge at the ferry landing place, or from the car park at the Gloucester end of the town. We have already mentioned the beauties of Newnham as seen from Arlingham Passage. To my mind it shares with Shropshire's Bridgnorth the title of Severn's loveliest town.

The beautifully coloured face of GARDEN HILL CLIFF, sometimes called Golden Cliff, enhances half a mile of river frontage near WESTBURY-ON-SEVERN, standing in delightful relief above the low and level banks on either side. Its sky-line, draped with foliage, rises gently along its length to a peak near its downstream end, then plunges steeply to bank level at the STRAND—and if London laughs loudest, let Westbury laugh last, for this really *is* a strand, overlooking the wide and tide-swept estuary. It overlooks, in fact, the sands of Pimlico.

From the Strand one can watch the bore sweep round the shore from Broadoak, its flank breaking over stonework placed to protect the frontage in 1949 for three-quarters of a mile downstream of Westbury Mill. Whether a bore is included or not, I strongly recommend the view from the top of Garden Hill Cliff, or when one is certain that no tide is due, a delightful little ramble is to walk the beach from the Strand to the Rodley end of the cliff and return along the top.

Having already mentioned the road-side viewing points of Minsterworth, little more need be said regarding specific places of easy, or relatively easy, access by road. But the eight miles of river below Gloucester, throughout which the bore is at its best, is fully accessible to all who like a country ramble, and to these the spectacle will be most impressive, for they will see it as it should be seen—deep in the heart of the country, away from crowds.

Yes, the chief thing is to get away from crowds if you can. Their very force of numbers and 'fun-of-the-fair' atmosphere positively insulate against the wonder, majesty and the awe-inspiring power of the bore. To a crowd the bore is a 'good 'un' if someone gets drenched and we all have a good laugh. But that's not it. Just what the real sensation is I cannot put in words. Thrill and wonder mingle with awe and something akin to fear—not fear of the bore, but of being in the presence of some relentless and irresistible power. I have seen many hundreds of bores and older riverside dwellers have seen many more, yet the feeling we share is always fresh and basically the same, however poorly we express it. For you to share this too is only a matter of taking the trouble to stroll across a few fields. The effort will be amply rewarded. Generally the going is easy and pleasant; but one should be suitably shod, for the grass is wet with dew if not with rain on spring and autumn mornings.

Finally, I have a request to make of all who seek the bore in lonely places, yet I know these are the very ones to whom the appeal is least necessary, for they love the countryside and respect its traditions. In an age when so many establishments keep toy policemen at their gates lest the 'unauthorised' should tread their sacred soil, we often overlook that fields are private property. Farmers are amazingly tolerant to allow their means of livelihood to be used for the pleasure of all and sundry without so much as 'by your leave'. All they ask is that their property shall not be abused. So please leave gates as you find them and do not walk or drive through growing crops.

Often we find old bottles left against floodbanks by previous tides. Throw them into the river by all means, but please don't break them where they lie; broken glass in fields is fiendish stuff for man, beast or child to tread upon and cannot be seen when the grass has grown a little.

May you have fair weather and many a mighty bore!

Chapter 5

RIDING THE BORE

Severnside men of Minsterworth, Elmore Back and lower down in my earlier years would take their boats, ride out the bore and let the flood stream carry them to Gloucester; they would do their shopping and drift home on the ebb. We of the river deal with the bore as a matter of course and use the tides to serve our ends, but I cannot stress too strongly how foolish, if not fatal, it would be for the uninitiated to attempt the same.

With the rise in popularity of small boat sailing and the ease with which light craft can be transported, the day is sure to come when a car will halt beside the Severn, say at Minsterworth, and someone will fancy a trip on the river. Why is it, in an age when no one is allowed to drive or fly without training, examination and licensing, that any fool with a boat is allowed to sail the sea, flirt with the tides of dangerous estuaries, or mess about on busy rivers? Totally unskilled, they are free to jeopardise their lives and the lives of their companions, and bring danger and hardship to those impelled in the name of humanity to attempt rescues for which the need should never have arisen.

The really capable boatman or boatwoman, however, is presumed to have sufficient water-sense to adapt the art of boat-handling to the needs of any particular situation, especially if fore-warned of what that situation will demand. So, if your ability is up to standard and you will accept the advice of an old hand, launch your boat and ride a small bore in safety.

You will enjoy it. Then graduate to larger ones.

Having ridden bores large and small in everything from a canoe to a coal barge, I can state my preference for a good stout row-boat about fifteen feet by six. Power, useful as it may be for getting about, is no advantage when riding the bore in a small boat. My favourite means of propulsion is a good pair of oars, and if I am alone I like to stand up facing for-ard and push on them, bracing my knees against a thwart in the rough water. With passengers aboard I sit down, but the normal rowing position makes forward observation difficult, uncomfortable and intermittent. One might as well put a horse at a fence when seated backwards in the saddle. Besides, you miss the thrill of watching every second of your adversary's advance, or stand a good chance of being so hypnotised by the thing that you let the boat go all over the place and make a thorough hash of the whole manœuvre. To scull over the stern is all very well until, just when most control is needed, the bore knocks the sweep out of the score (the oar out of the sculling notch). If you have but one oar, best use it as a paddle. Speed is not needed, but control of direction is essential. A paddle, of course, is the proper thing if you use one of those wonderfully stable Severn fishing punts, strong as a battleship and nearly as heavy.

Imagine we are going down-river in a fifteen-footer to meet the bore. Come aboard at Lower Parting—a dirty business, I'm afraid, on these high muddy banks—and as we row downstream I'll explain the procedure.

This morning's tide at Sharpness is 9.9 metres at ten past ten; the river two feet above summer level and the wind south-westerly and moderate. All this promises a reasonably good bore and it should be up to time. For comfort and safety we do not want to encounter the bore at just any place. When that cannot be avoided we make the best of it, but today we are demonstrating the proper way, so we will keep to the general rule of meeting the bore at a selected place and allowing adequate time to get there. We must avoid being in shallow water, for that would mean a breaking bore and possible danger. Yet our quest for deep water must not take us to the outside of a sharp bend; true, the water will be deeper there, but the bore will be too big and boisterous for safety.

I am making for that long, easy bend midway between Lower Parting and Manor Ditch. The water there is deep enough, and the bend not so sharp as to prevent a reasonable view down-river, so we shall not be caught unawares but have sufficient time to study the approaching bore and get into the best position for tackling it. The point about choosing a gentle bend is that if the bore's low side does not look exciting enough we shall have time to move over and ride a higher part. I think we shall be all right in mid-stream today.

Another point about a long, easy bend is the time factor. To forecast the exact moment of the bore's arrival at a place so remote from Sharpness is impossible. For it to turn up dead on time would be an accident, not expert calculation. So we must be prepared to kill ten minutes or so while remaining in suitable waters. Anchoring or going to the bank would invite disaster. Nor is it wise to kill time by turning and rowing upstream for a while; ten to one the bore will loom up behind, and in the flurry of swinging round the approach will be misjudged. Best hold the boat back on the oars if necessary. However, the long bend will provide all the latitude we need. We gauge our progress to bring us just within the bend five minutes ahead of zero time; then we can dawdle with the stream with the sure knowledge that, be it late or early, we shall encounter the bore somewhere within the curving length of river.

As soon as it comes in sight we shall decide whether we can ride the head in midstream or should keep more to its lower side. But there must be no dilly-dallying; we need a few moments to position ourselves, straighten up, and get braced for the rough passage. Too late to change our minds when the bore is almost upon us; we cannot avoid it, so better meet any section head-on than be caught off-square changing our station. We shall tackle the waves of the bore much as we should deal with those of a rough sea, meeting them exactly head-on. But with bore waves we have also to cope with the sudden reversal of the flow and the immediate transformation of the river from a placid downward-flowing stream to a choppy, turbulent, upward-racing torrent.

Taken squarely, the leading wave will not really bother us. The bows will rear up and we may feel the boat thrown backwards; in fact a good pull on the oars may be needed to coax her over and prevent us driving back stern-first. But allowing the boat to be somewhat set a-back is quite intentional. One should never try to surmount the bore by charging at it. Like a boxer who eases the impact of an opponent's blow by riding back with it, being set a-back by the first wave eases our encounter with the second and succeeding waves, which are often the more dangerous.

Then we shall—— But hold everything; here she comes—and a beauty, too! See what I mean about her swinging to the outside bank? Nine or ten feet high that side, but only a foot or so against the inner bank. We shall be all right in mid-stream; barely three feet there, I should think. Steady! Steady! Hold on! Up we go then! A good pull—and over! Slap down into the face of the second wave, sinking the prow to the sheer-strake and shipping a drop of water. An instant of apprehension and the bows leap for the sky, miss it and topple down to plunge into the third wave. Over, and into the fourth, less high; and the fifth, but with decreasing violence, merging into the wild and choppy aftermath—a race of broken water slapping our sides from all directions.

That was the Severn bore! The rough ride lasted barely a minute; less time than it takes to describe it, but far more exciting to experience.

How different everything looks now! No more high banks mirrored in calm water. We have risen so much the banks are only half their height, and the rough water has already swept us far upstream of where we met the bore. Things will ease down presently, and I shall be able to put you ashore at about the place where you embarked.

No two boats will handle quite the same, and no two bores be just identical; but the routine I have described will bring you safely through big bores in average boats. Even so, I am not recommending anyone to tackle a big bore first, nor any first bore unaccompanied by a local river-man. Nevertheless, an able boat-handler could start off on his own by riding the bore of a tide not exceeding 8.5 metres at Sharpness, just to get the idea. Then he might graduate to bigger ones. But he should not venture below Minsterworth, and at low water must avoid the rocks at the Denny, Minsterworth Church, Stonebench and Little Bench. Also he should keep clear of that tempting straight mile from Manor Ditch down to Upper Rea; it is usually much too shallow. Finally, do not ride the bore so near to Gloucester as to run the risk of being swept by the following tide against the bridges or the weirs.

During the years when I was more afloat than on the shore, being engaged in hydrographic survey, I rode several hundred bores in cabin cruisers, first in the *Pioneer* and then the *Fairylight,* both of the River Severn Catchment Board. With bores of all sizes coming along day and night, summer and winter, fair weather and foul, in daylight, moonlight or pitch darkness, one just got used to them; not that any could be ignored, and big ones made particular demands. We remained tied up at our berth for only the very smallest bores. Even then the sharp lurch of the boat put heavy strains on ropes and cleats.

The technique of riding the bore in a cabin cruiser is much the same as for rowing boats. I can recall having 'nasty moments' with only two bores, both very big ones, both in darkness and both, as it happens, near Lower Parting. The first was when we had the *Pioneer,* manned by myself and three hands, living aboard.

Countrymen in my youth defined dark nights as when the outline of the trees above you cannot be seen against the sky.

(8) *As the bore-rider sees it*

(9) *Splashing against the protruding tumps*

(10) *A wall of water*

Such nights are rare, and even more rarely is there not the faintest sheen of light upon a stretch of water—which is why, incidentally, some navigation buoys are painted black to show up better in the dark. But one February night it was so dark on the river that nothing showed at all; the banks being lined with trees did not help. A low glass and westerly gale gave just the conditions to amplify the very high tides and bring an outsize bore. In addition it was raining torrents, which accounted for the extra-special darkness.

We had tied up at our berth at Llanthony, below the weir at Gloucester, after a day's work in bad weather on the morning tide, from which we had wrenched some of its secrets. We could not retreat out of harm's way above the weirs, thanks to a state of things that allows a barrier of weirs to be maintained across the river but lets the locks go permanently derelict. The bore was due at five past ten and there was nothing to do but go and ride it out as usual. Soon after nine we left the berth for a suitable location—in fact the long, gentle bend below Lower Parting already mentioned. The bore would certainly be early, so I was allowing more time than usual.

By keeping near the bank it was possible to grope down the narrow East Channel to the Parting, but once out in the wide main river I found myself with little or no sense of position or direction. My idea of mid-river was an absolute guess and as I started cruising slowly to meet the bore the only thing I knew for certain was that we were not, at any rate, going upstream. With the noise of engine, wind and rain there was no hope of hearing the approaching bore, and in the darkness still less chance of seeing it. Early it would be for sure; but just how early no-one could conjecture—ten minutes maybe, or five; perhaps fifteen. We must be ready all the time and braced for it.

I was uneasy: were we in the middle of the river or to one side or to the other? It was desperately necessary to take the low side of the bore tonight, so I kept a starboard tendency, to take us, I hoped, towards the right-hand bank and safety. That sort of craft, however, with much more top-hamper than draught, would not hold course too well in gusty side-winds at low speed. As a forlorn hope I switched on the old car head-lamp listed as a 'searchlight' in our inventory, and put a man on deck to swing it round and look. A yellowish beam played on a maze of rain-drops and lost itself down an alley of glittering needles.

'Where are we?' I yelled.

'In a bottle of Indian ink!'

Just as I thought. But I might have called it red ink!

Out with the light. Darkness was less confusing, though alive with fancies.

'Reckon we're too near the right bank,' sang a voice from up above. So I put her to port a little, still dead slow ahead.

Then it happened! We must have been well on the wrong side of the river, where the bore was at its highest; and miles off-square, heading obliquely for the bank. A brief loud hissing heralded the crash. An avalanche of water broke on the starboard bow and smothered us. Up reared the bows impossibly, reaching a hideous angle and canting to port as the *Pioneer* squatted on her stern, pressing the cockpit gun'le under water. And she hung like it, driving grotesquely backwards and over as to destruction, with water pouring in.

A blind instinct made me seize the throttle, open it up and put the wheel a-starboard. The engine growled and spluttered, gave a kick—and stopped. But it was enough—or had Another Agent intervened? Down came the bows, the stern lifted and we were washed drunkenly through the seething crest to smash broadside into the second leading wave, which rolled us on our side and hurled us everywhere before it let us drop beneath a third enormous wave. . . . Next I remember wallowing in the aftermath, dazed by the wild succession of assaults, hanging on numbly to the stricken boat, which now rolled waterlogged and crippled in the darkness, adrift in the racing tide. Awareness of reality returned. We were still afloat!

A form beside me coughed. Someone said 'Gaud Almighty!' I called to the man who could not possibly be still on deck:

'You there, Dick?'

'Aye, skip.'

'Can you get for'ard and let go the hook?'

'I'll try, skip.'

As external sounds subsided we heard the din of pots, pans, crocks, cans, stoves, buckets, floorboards—everything—all swilling and crashing about together in the flooded cabin as we rolled. In the cockpit, a step above the cabin floor, water was halfway up to our knees. Were we sinking? Had we been stove in?

The loud rattle of cable paying out was welcome. Presently the anchor jagged, broke out, then caught again and held. The quick jerk and swing of the bows to stem the tide told how fast we had been drifting. I centred the helm. The rolling almost ceased. But the water round our legs seemed deeper.

'Pump like hell! Find the buckets, Pat, and the baler.'

He forced open the jammed doors of the cabin and waded in.

'Lights won't work. Gi'me a torch. Ta. Cripes, what a mess! Buckets, you said? One Sunday suit; tin o' paraffin; tea-pot. Ah! bucket. Got him! Bucket coming! Frying pan; somebody's pillow; here's the baler—no, it's the jerry; one tooth brush; primus; writing pad; here, skip, *Manual of Tides* coming up!'

'Blast the tides! Let's have another bucket.'

'Here we come; soon have her dry!'

And so we did. She was not holed.

Pat found the oil lamp but 'couldn't get him lit'. He was luckier with the primus, finding meth. and paraffin well stoppered. The water-breaker was intact, too. The clankity-clank of the primus being pumped ferociously and the buzzing of its flame beneath a kettle heralded a return to something like normality, however far removed. Steaming hot cocoa arrived in two surviving mugs, a broken jug and a jam jar—and was never more welcome.

High water passed and the *Pioneer* swung on her anchor to the ebb. The rain had stopped and the gale seemed to have blown itself out. The sky was full of stars. You often find the weather changes with the tide; I can't account for it. A clock in the town struck midnight; eight bells, and all's comparatively well! Two of us spent the rest of the long night dismantling the engine and drying its essential parts. By dawn, with our torch batteries almost expended, we had it running. The other two had straightened things in the cabin and bundled up all that must go ashore for drying. But the best thing was the glorious odour from the galley! Broken eggs and bacon, with sopping bread fried in dripping, and tea in unusual vessels, another mug having been broken in the night.

We cruised back to Llanthony. Our ever-good friends at the Lock House took in our wet bundles to dry them, and gave us fresh water. A wash and a shave, then off down-river to do some work before the morning bore and tide.

The second time I nearly came to grief was several years later, in the *Fairylight*. This was a different phase of operations. The personnel had changed and no-one lived aboard. When being used below Gloucester the *Fairylight* was often based at the *Pioneer's* old berth at Llanthony, which was all very well except that having no resident crew meant someone having to turn out specially to tend her night-times and week-ends when big tides were running. For small and medium bores we devised a way of mooring her in midstream by four lines so that she could ride unattended, but after having our moorings tampered with we watched her on each occasion. For big bores, however, there was nothing for it but to cruise her down to our old rendezvous below Lower Parting and ride them out in traditional manner, returning to the berth almost immediately. Having a car, it was easier for me to turn up than for most of the men; also it was not a responsibility I cared to delegate. So I did the night and week-end trips myself and never lacked a volunteer to form my crew of one.

On a September night, when equinoxial tides were at their maximum and again a south-west gale betokened a monster bore, I turned out to do the chore with Jesse Trigg—a fine fellow with boats and engines and with no fear of the bore, having been born and bred with it rolling past his doorstep at the Noards, near Minsterworth. We checked fuel, started the engine, checked circulating water, slipped moorings and set off steadily down the East Channel, allowing ample time in case the bore was unduly early. The night was dark but not pitch black; in any case the darkness had little bearing on subsequent events, merely adding to the confusion.

Frankly, although we called them 'a bit of a bind', we rather enjoyed these trips. They were simple routine operations and on the night in question Jesse and I were chatting casually when, less than halfway to the Parting, the engine began to sound rough. A moment later it was knocking badly. A plume of steam hissed from the water outlet and a hot smell rose from the engine casing. We switched off. I kept the boat on course as we lost way while Jesse looked for the trouble, suspecting the water pump. But no; the stoppage was on the inlet side of the pump. In a matter of moments Jesse had lifted the floorboards and whipped out the pipe between pump and sea-cock, only to find it perfectly clear, while the sea-cock, still full open, was dry. Clearly the external strainer under the hull was choked—and we guessed how this had come about, having just passed the Gloucester crude sewage outfall which disgorged no small proportion of waterlogged paper, about which we need not go into detail.

The strainer itself was inaccessible, of course, and poking wire down through the sea-cock from the inside had no effect. By now the boat had lost all way and was drifting with no control at all. Our margin of time was running out. If we could not get going within five minutes we should have to tie up to a tree, get out and leave the *Fairylight* to her fate, with a more than even chance of losing her. Five minutes; at the very outside.

I did not see how Jesse did it; I was up on deck trying to catch the sound of the bore in the distance, but the wind was too boisterous. I believe he connected the pipe and blew down it, or something. Whatever it was, the water gushed and he called for me as he completed the connection to the pump. The engine had cooled, and within seconds we had it running and were under power again. She was a fast boat and I reckoned if we hurried we had just time to reach the Parting; with luck we might get well beyond. I opened the throttle and went flat out.

The East Channel is narrow throughout, but just as it ends it curves sharply to the left and there is such an extensive shoal off the left bank that at low water a boat like the *Fairylight* has to hug close against the very outside of the bend to find enough water; the only route, but the worst possible place to meet a bore. We went tearing round this final bend.

We lost the race by the skin of our teeth; and by the same token we escaped destruction. Within yards of our objective an enormous hill of water loomed out of the darkness, towering so high on our side of the river that its ragged crest was toppling in the night sky above us. Our speed, with that of the river, must have been twelve miles an hour; and the bore's about the same.

If you can imagine a cabin cruiser charging headlong into a ten-foot wave, steep and about to break, at a nett speed of twenty-four miles an hour, you may wonder how we or the boat survived. I do yet. The collision was terrific. I believe we went clean through the first wave. The bows went down instead of up and gave the sensation of diving to the bottom. Certainly the wheel-house was submerged. Then up she came, broke surface steeply and pitch-poled wallop over the second wave—or was it the third?

We finished up wedged beneath the branches of a willow tree, from which nasty position we extricated ourselves by brute force, though it was touch and go against the rapid rise of tide. Once free, we got a line on a branch and made fast, with breathing space to sort ourselves out. The engine had stopped, of course, and we had shipped an awful lot of water. As for the cabin interior, it looked as if we had gone over Niagara Falls. But thanks to a teak hull and strong frames we had sustained no vital damage. I will not dwell on the details of how we returned to berth at Llanthony in the small hours of the morning, nor on the major hardship of having, this time, no means of brewing a drink.

One summer in the 1930s I had the loan of a Canadian-type canoe, the sort with turned-up ends and much more beam than one might think. I used it mostly upstream of Gloucester but succumbed to the temptation to try the bore in it. Bores are not very big at that time of year, but such as there were the canoe rode well, being used in much the same way as small boats. It was rather fun paddling along, but I was not especially thrilled, possibly because the bores themselves did not compare with those one can ride in a proper boat.

In the autumn of 1954 I was visited by one Colonel J. Churchill, a man brimming over with life and energy. He had been a Commando leader during the war and had just dashed up from Salisbury or somewhere to find out something about the bore. But his enquiries were not like those I am used to, so I asked outright what his special interest was, and for my pains got sworn to secrecy—an undertaking from which I was released only on the fulfilment of his enterprise. On my promise not to breathe a word to anyone the Colonel confided that he wanted to ride the bore on a surf-board. His desire to attempt the feat was equalled only by his wish to avoid publicity. Did I think it a practical proposition? His enthusiasm was so infectious that I nearly said 'Lend me a surf-board and I'll find out!'

We went into the matter thoroughly, he as a surf-boarding expert and I with my knowledge of the bore, but the mechanics of the thing were not encouraging. It did not appear that the board would plane fast enough to stay on the surface without out-running the wave that supported it. Colonel Churchill would not be put off; he would use an Australian surf-board, he said, which is not the plain board I had in mind but has buoyancy compartments. This put a new aspect on things. We concluded that there was some chance of success and I supplied dates and times of suitable bores for an attempt to be made in the spring or summer of 1955.

At half past ten on the morning of 21 July 1955, Colonel Churchill swam out from the bank below Stonebench with his surf-board. There was a tide of 9.5 metres at Sharpness and as the fair-sized bore approached, the Colonel placed his board beneath him and began to swim upstream. Moments later the leading slope of the bore slid under him and he started planing forward. By leg movements and balance the intrepid rider exercised a measure of control. The Colonel had hoped he might ride for miles and all was going fairly well when the bore ran into shallower water on Stonebench rock and broke, completely upsetting surf-board and rider. Colonel Churchill had a very rugged time swimming to the shore and was severely tossed about in dragging his surf-board through the wild confusion of the bore's aftermath. He was determined to try again the following year. I believe nothing but an overseas posting would have prevented him, but I have not seen him since. Skilled surfers in later years have done better. Rodney Sumpter rode quite well in 1967, then in 1970 a team from the A.A. magazine 'Drive' managed two miles. Australian surfers have had varying successes but the record to date is held by Colin Wilson, whose ride of nearly three miles is recorded in the I.T.V. film 'The Longest Wave'. Riding up with the bore en masse in kayaks is a sport pioneered by Eric Wynter.

A brief word on swimming the bore will not be out of place in a chapter on riding the bore; and brief is all it need be, for the enterprise has nothing to commend it. Only a very powerful swimmer can be sure of surviving; this is a fight for life. Many have lost. Swimming the bore is the least satisfying of all the ways of meeting it. Practically no sensation is derived from medium-sized unbroken bores, whereas big ones provide nothing more than a dirty mix-up, with a lot of splashy discomfiture ending in a miserable scramble up the filthy bank to get out, and a dripping quarter-mile trudge back to where you left your clothes. No; I do not recommend it. What I do recommend—and should have done earlier—is that no-one should attempt to ride the bore in any manner who is not a strong swimmer.

I had quite an exciting ride on 2 December 1959, when filming for B.B.C. television. The bore really turned up trumps, though I feared the occasion would frighten it off. Cameraman Jim Saunders sat in the stern of the boat with a battery-driven camera while Producer Ron Webster used a spring-motored camera on the shore. It was cold waiting in mid-stream, and a shade colder when the bore's distant thunder betrayed its size long before its head came crashing round the bend. A beauty! Jim raised his camera as the wave drove on relentlessly towards us. At forty yards it made a wondrous sight, rising to six feet high as it met the shallower water where we lay.

One's eye is less than three feet high when seated in a boat. One looks up at a big bore, and at thirty yards this one looked as big as I could handle. They tell me I either sing or talk to myself when on the river, but I was silent, I'm sure, when I saw that wave-front steepen to an ominous curl at fifteen yards. Then—'Hell! she's breaking,' I yelled. Jim squatted stolidly, camera glued to face, as the toppling wall reared over us. Thoughts of disaster and my Waterloo bothered my concentration as I braced for the mighty tussle I must win. Up shot the bows and I plunged the oars firmly in the slope, heaving to the last ounce of strength and weight. They held as if set in concrete as the boat slid back while I pulled forwards. We hung there till I thought the oars would break. Such was our angle that I nearly fell forward on to Jim below me in the stern, keeping his lens over the bows but photographing in those tense moments, as the film proved, the clear sky overhead.

At last! Over the crest and a sickening drop to the trough, plunging stem-deep in the second wave, and up again. So to the sixth and seventh wave, fighting them all and revelling in mastery. Now I was singing loud and happy as a king.

'How's that!' I called to Jim. He didn't answer.

Once through the aftermath I made for the bank.

'Like it, Jim?' I said.

'O Lord!' was all he said; and I count him one of the bravest, for I confess I would not for all the tea in China ride any bore as passenger; even less could I work a camera all the time as he did.

'I crept into the eye-piece for safety,' he told me later; and I learned that the B.B.C. had been very concerned for the safety of—the camera!

Two River Board men, Jack Cale and Sam Jennings, had been working nearby and came running as we climbed ashore. They seemed truly relieved to find the 'old man' safe!

'Gosh! You went right out of sight! Never thought you'd come through it,' said Jack, to which Sam added, 'We nearly parted company, boss.' Gentle Sam! His words came back to me four years later as I stood in the snow-clad little churchyard above the river at Hempsted. We had parted company.

The film of that ride has been shown several times. Once, while being interviewed on another tidal matter I glanced in the monitor and saw myself, not as I was, but riding that bore again. Then it was used when I did a studio piece on the bore, using the model mentioned earlier and chatting a little. This was on the West Region, but when I was asked to repeat it for the Midlands, live, in *Scan,* there was nearly a hiatus. Magazine programmes often use several 'sets' in one large studio, the cameras and so on moving from set to set, item by item. My model was all set up, filled with water and well rehearsed. Transmission of the preceding item neared its end when a mobile camera, trucking back to range on my set, struck the model. Something cracked and water spurted on to the studio floor. Frantically, even while being announced, I worked with my fingers pushing black bitumastic into the leak from nearby joints. Then I was 'on'. The loss of water affected the bore a little, and I performed with both hands plastered in filthy bitumen and my feet in a puddle. But viewers didn't know.

The next ride for television was on a frosty morning of 26 February 1963. This was not filmed but video-recorded at Bristol from equipment on the site at Upper Rea. The tide predicted was two feet higher than the time before, but I was glad it produced a much smaller bore, for the little boat was laden to the gun'le with equipment and like a porcupine with aerials. There was the cameraman, myself, a hand television camera, a television transmitter, two-way sound radio between cameraman and producer, a radio transmitter for me to do a commentary, plus a load of great batteries—all in a fifteen-footer. I was fenced in with sprouting aerials and wore a lanyard microphone round my neck. They tied the lead of this securely to the boat—to ensure, perhaps, that if I muffed the ride I would be dragged to the bottom by the neck.

That bore, as I said, was nothing special; just worth riding but rather tame. We had a technical success, however, though I have not seen the result.

Quite unprecedented was the scene on 14 April 1964, when Harry Head's *Regent Lady,* the River Board's barge *Riparian* and the Board's survey launch, forming a small armada, all rode the bore together off Minsterworth Ferry. A very different armada, consisting of some twenty kayaks of the Worcester Canoe Club, assembled off Newham on 4 May 1969 to 'race' up river to Minsterworth with the bore, or just behind it, filmed by the B.B.C. This became an annual event for some years.

Chapter 6

THE BORE AND THE BARGES

The bore's domain—the Severn between Gloucester and Sharpness—is commonly described as 'unnavigable'. This is libel or slander according to whether it is written down or spoken, as I understand the law. Whatever else Queen Elizabeth I might have done, she would not, I think, have Chartered a statutory Port on unnavigable waters, and the Severn below Gloucester has not so greatly changed since 20 June 1580, when she granted the Royal Charter which commissioned Gloucester as a Port, complete with Customs.

True, the constant shifting of deep-water channels, coupled with hazards of tide and bore, made navigation difficult, and as the age of speed began to dawn it was inconvenient that tides flow to Gloucester only one week out of every two. Ultimately, with the size of sea-going ships ever increasing, a more consistent route was needed to the old established Port, and this was effected when the Gloucester & Sharpness Ship Canal was opened on 26 April 1827, by-passing the Severn between its terminals at Gloucester and Sharpness. But dues were levied on the canal whereas the river was free, so for many more years there was traffic on the river though in decreasing quantity. Just within my own memory occasional cargoes of coal from the Forest of Dean were shipped from Bullo Dock to Framilode lock, thence inland on the Stroudwater Canal.

Every navigable river of importance has evolved a type of vessel specially suited to its own peculiarities. We had the

Mersey flat, the Humber keel, the Norfolk wherry, the Thames barge and, on the Severn, the famous trow. Trows were wooden sailing vessels (a few were iron), mostly 40 to 60 tons capacity. They could navigate the often shallow upper reaches or the often stormy waters of the estuary and Bristol Channel; they could lie aground when necessary or ride the bore if they had to. They sailed to the Midlands if winds were fair and were drifted under control upon the tide in calms; they were kedged or poled or pushed, they were towed high up the river by harnessed men or horses, or lower down by men in rowing boats—but they got there. . . .

Like the 'fishermen of England' renowned in song, the trowmen of the Severn laboured mightily, two to a boat and sometimes a boy to train. To these men alone the Midlands

Fig. 14—A Severn trow under full sail

and all Severnside towns owe more than can be told of their prosperity and development. That this present day, with all its power and modern aids, should call the river 'unnavigable' is unwittingly to pay the greatest tribute possible to all who have sailed upon it down the ages.

More correctly one would describe the Severn between Gloucester and Sharpness as 'no longer navigated as a commercial thoroughfare'. In the early 1930s Captain Walter Butt ran a cargo of grain up to Gloucester in the little motor barge *Pisgah*. This was an isolated trip, though not without significance, for barges were again to be seen on the river upstream of Sharpness, not carrying commerce to Gloucester but mainly delivering stone for the River Authority to protect flood banks and sea walls against erosion: a revival of an ancient trade, for it has been customary from time immemorial to protect the banks in this manner. Frequently the last use for which a trow was deemed fit was the stone trade, and at her very end she made one final trip laden with stone to be scuttled and form a breakwater. You will find them yet, some still intact, though many have burst asunder or been silted into the bank and almost lost. These must not be confused with the old hulks in the trow 'graveyards' at Purton and Lydney.

Perhaps I may be forgiven a feeling of quiet satisfaction that, with early memories of stone-bearing trows in mind, I was instrumental in re-starting the trade with motor barges in the mid-1930s for the Severn Catchment Board, thus keeping alive the historic art of navigating this part of the River Severn. After two years of living on the river, studying its tides, surveying its channels and mixing with surviving trowmen, I was convinced that what had been done under sail could now be carried out with powered vessels. Much stone was urgently needed after years of neglect and I felt I had acquired the ability to direct the operation.

The Catchment Board entered into a contract with the Captain Butt already mentioned, and he pioneered the revival. In the early days he picked me up below Sharpness and we ran to sites as far upstream as Minsterworth; always, or so it seemed, in torrential rain! Captain Butt started off with the iron Dutch-built barge *Sunrisen,* but for most of his contracts he used the *River King* which was brought round from Hull and proved a useful craft. At one time he brought into service the old trow *Ripple,* fitted with twin yacht engines, to deliver stone from a jetty built just below Llanthony weir.

Subsequent contractors trading from the Wye have used a variety of vessels. There was the Mersey flat *Protection,* the Barnstaple sand barge *Mary* and the Humber keel *Elmdale.* At one time the *Protection* towed the Severn trow *Victory.* The large motor vessel *Fir* ran a few cargoes to Awre. Then Harry Head used the converted tanker *Severn Traveller,* and Fred Larkham skippered the *Regent Lady.*

These vessels loaded in the Wye, but to serve the river between Gloucester and Bollow it was found more convenient to load at Minsterworth and distribute from there. The Catchment Board used its own butty-boat *Jupiter,* towed by the *Fairylight,* and in 1939 Mr Christopher March of Worcester employed his motor long-boat (or narrow-boat) *Heatherbelle,* delightfully painted in traditional style. I remember piloting him up to Gloucester, under the comb-like structure of the temporary road-bridge at Maisemore and over Maisemore weir on the morning tide the day war broke out, having heard Mr Chamberlain's fateful announcement by radio at the berth at Minsterworth. A year later *Heatherbelle* was down again, this time with an all-lady crew —Miss Daphne March, sister of the owner (who was serving at sea), and Mrs Molly Trail, with occasionally the mother of the owner—surely the first and, so far, the only wholly female crew to work a trading vessel on this tide-swept length of Severn.

In 1943 the Catchment Board (which was to become the River Board in 1950) acquired its own motor long-boat *Venus,* in which several thousand tons of stone were transported to the river banks between Gloucester and Bollow. In April 1963 the River Board's new motor barge *Riparian*—meaning 'to do with the banks of a river', and specially designed and built for the job—came up the Severn from Sharpness and started work in the Minsterworth/Elmore area. There, of course, she had to ride every bore that ran, day and night all the year round, much as we did in the old *Pioneer* and *Fairylight,* but more comfortably. For her first dry-docking I brought her on a suitable tide over Llanthony weir in March 1964, and she became the first of her kind to complete the river trip from Sharpness to Gloucester Docks, without the use of Llanthony lock.

The fifteen vessels I have named have all traded on the so-called 'unnavigable' portion of the Severn since the mid-thirties, and like their forebears have had to deal with the bore.

One might think the bore would be a major hazard of barge navigation, but in fact it is not. It has to be dealt with, of course, and has caused some accidents and disasters in by-gone years, but when encountered it is quickly disposed of and forms but little part of the journey in hand. Thus, in records of navigation, as in conversation with old trowmen, the bore is rarely mentioned. Times of tide, depths of water, strengths of currents, winds, good or bad anchorages—these are of far greater significance to the bargemaster.

When the Severn sailor comes up from Sharpness to Gloucester he does not so much as see the bore; he 'carries his tide' right through—a single tide carries his vessel all the way. The bore of that tide has gone on well ahead. If only the peak of high water moved up the river more slowly the trip would be dead easy, for a powered barge could go all the way literally 'on the crest of the wave'—the tide-wave, of course, not the bore—simply by keeping pace with it. But it will outstrip any vessel, so when bound for Gloucester the bargemaster must leave Sharpness about forty minutes before high water at that place in order to arrive at Gloucester not too long after high

(11) *It may break but will gather again*

(12) *Bore progressing from right to left on N.E. limb of Horseshoe Bend*

(13) *Trow 'Ripple' berthing at the jetty below Llanthony weir, Gloucester*

(14) *Tidal model of the River Severn, at the Hydraulics Research Station, Wallingford*

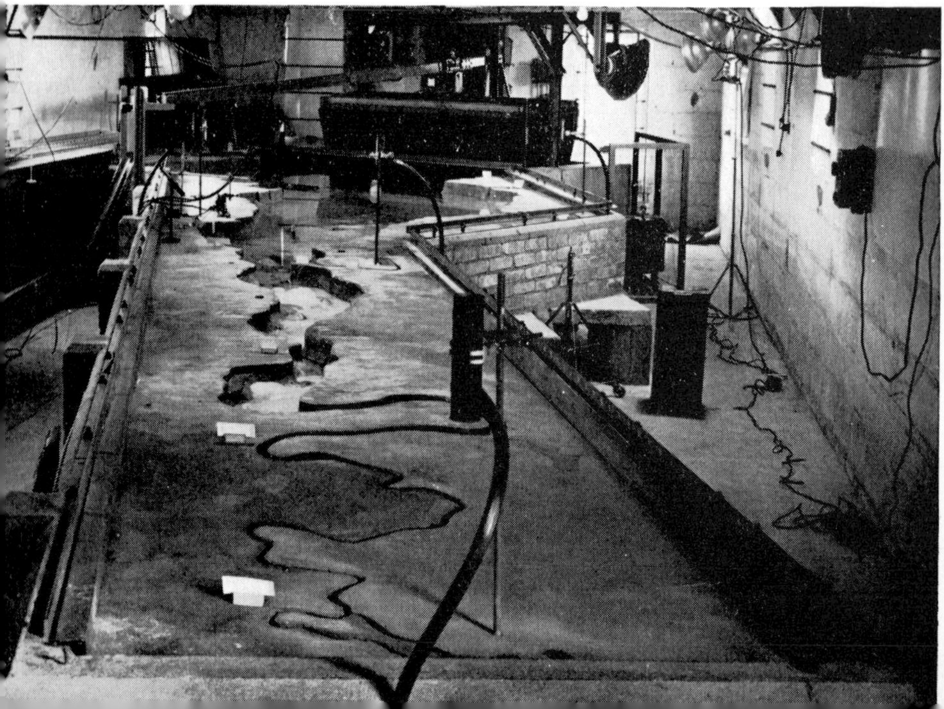

water there. His great care throughout, apart from keeping in the deep channels, is to gauge his speed in relation to the passage of high water so that he secures the best possible conditions at the most difficult places. One of the worst places is right up at Longney Sands and he dearly likes to get there slightly before high water, when he will have almost the maximum depth but a little rise in hand to float him off should he have the misfortune to run aground. Sailing barges had to leave Sharpness considerably earlier, of course. Once over Longney Sands and up to Bollow the master knows he will have ample water all the way to Gloucester even if the tide begins to 'come down on him' before he gets there.

The return from Gloucester to Sharpness is very different. Whereas one can come up on one tide-wave there is no such wave to go back on. A sailing vessel cannot leave Gloucester much before high water; even a powered barge can make but slow headway against the strong flood tide. Not until after high water, when the stream has turned and the ebb gathered strength, can the vessel make any speed. By then the tide has been ebbing two hours at Sharpness and even as the boat proceeds it is running to where there is more and more ebb, so by the time it reaches Bollow there is not enough tide-water left to give it draught over the next shallow, Longney Sands. It must therefore lie up at Bollow and cannot continue its journey until the next tide is nearly full. One is not surprised to find at Bollow a former inn, the Sloop, now a private house.

But how much better that you should hear about the trip direct from a genuine trowmaster of the past. I can quote his very words, taken down verbatim in the late afternoon of 19 February 1849, when he gave evidence at an Admiralty Enquiry in the old Tolsey, at Gloucester. So faithfully were his words recorded that even his dialect mispronunciation of place names has been preserved.

Joseph Robinson was a retired trow-master. For 42 years he had plied the Severn between the Midlands and the Bristol Channel ports. On 'swallowing the anchor' he had been appointed tollkeeper at Gloucester. Here is an extract from his evidence, the words in parenthesis being mine:

'Inspectors.—Well, going down the river, when you start from Gloucester, you go a little before high water?—Yes, about ten minutes. (Being bow-hauled from Llanthony lock to Lower Parting to get under way in the main river with the first of the ebb.)

That takes you down to Bolo (Bollow) Pool?—Yes, we stop there till the next tide.

What is the nature of the bottom there?—Sand.

Is there any part that is rock at the bottom?—At the head of it, and where the sand is off, the bottom is hard gravel.

Where does the next tide take you?—To Priden. (Pridings)

Have you sufficient water to keep afloat there?—Yes.

What is the nature of the bottom there?—Hard marl, very good anchorage.

Not stone?—No.

Not the rock marl?—No.

If there is no wind, do you drop down with the tide?—Yes, with boats; we have large boats with four or six men in them, and we are towed there.

Is your crew there?—Generally we take one or two men to assist.

Then with the third tide, where do you go?—To Hamstell. (Hamstalls.) It generally depends on the wind.

You are generally able to go from Priden to Hamstell in a tide?—Yes.

And do you pass any hard rock in that distance?—Yes.

Where does it occur?—At a place called Harlingham. (Arlingham.)

What is the Harlingham Rock, does it ever pick you up? —Yes, that is very bad; there is sand on the other side of it. If the wind is southward or westward we generally go on shore at Brick Hills. (This last sentence concludes his reply to the earlier question as to where he went on the third tide.)

Have you any rocks on that side?—Yes, very hard rocks nearly all the way down.

You don't go down without a fair wind?—Oh, yes, we beat down sometimes. They'll beat with a head wind from the Brick Hills all the way to King's Road. (King Road, off Avonmouth.)

With the wind right ahead?—Yes, I have known vessels drawing seven feet of water that I have beat down from Hamstell to King's Road.

Coming up, do you go to the same stations?—No, we generally make our stations from King's Road in the spring time to Bolo Pool, and sometimes to Gloucester. I have several times made my passage from the bay of Newport to this place (Gloucester); I once run with a vessel drawing five feet of water in five hours and twenty-five minutes. (About sixty river miles.)'

Thus a sailing vessel, like a powered barge, could make the upward run on one tide. But it took four tides to get back, whereas a well-powered vessel by punching hard against the flood tide can return in two, making its station at Pridings, or thereabouts. At some stations, Pridings being one of them, barges have to meet the bore afloat. A sailing vessel would do so at anchor—note Joseph Robinson's emphasis on the good anchorage at Pridings—but a powered barge can be swung round before tide and meet the bore under gentle power. At other stations, such as Brick Hills, a vessel would arrive while there was still sufficient tide-water left for it to ground on a shelf of mud against the bank several feet above low water level. There it would lie too high to be touched by the next bore and would not refloat until the tide had risen six or seven feet and the turbulence of the early tide-race had subsided. On China's Chiang tang kiang such 'shelves' are made artificially for vessels to lie up and avoid the monster bore of that river.

The great thing is to be either well afloat or well aground; to be only just afloat or only just aground will result in the vessel being lifted and dropped heavily on the bottom by each of the bore's waves and possibly severely damaged.

The time of lying up between the ebb of one tide and the bore of the next was the trowman's only chance to snatch a little sleep; but he must not over-sleep. I have mentioned in an earlier chapter that the riverman's time-table is the tide-table. Do you know his alarm-clock? Whether lying afloat or aground he would have an anchor down, but not all the cable —a heavy chain—would have been paid out, only just enough to hold the barge against the last of the ebb. This length of cable would be 'stopped' or held to the barge merely by pushing a stout stick through a link just inboard of the hawse-pipe (Fig. 15). A sufficient additional length of cable to hold the vessel against the powerful flood tide would then be flaked out on deck with the ultimate end properly secured. Then the crew would 'turn in'. When tide arrived the strong tug on the cable would snap the stick and allow the extra cable to go rattling along the deck and out through the hawse-pipe, creating a noise below that would wake the dead! The device could not fail to function, because the size of the cable link limited the size of the stick pushed through it to one that could not resist the great pull of the flood tide.

But is anything infallible? When Ernie Wyman and Fred Larkham were running the wooden *Mary* on Catchment Board work they were shaken from sleep not by the rattle of the cable but by a mighty cracking beneath them, and looking down they saw the fluke of their anchor sticking up through the cabin floor! In dense fog the barge had drifted over her anchor before settling down. It took ages to cut the fluke off with a hack-saw, but the ugly hole was roughly boarded over before the new tide came.

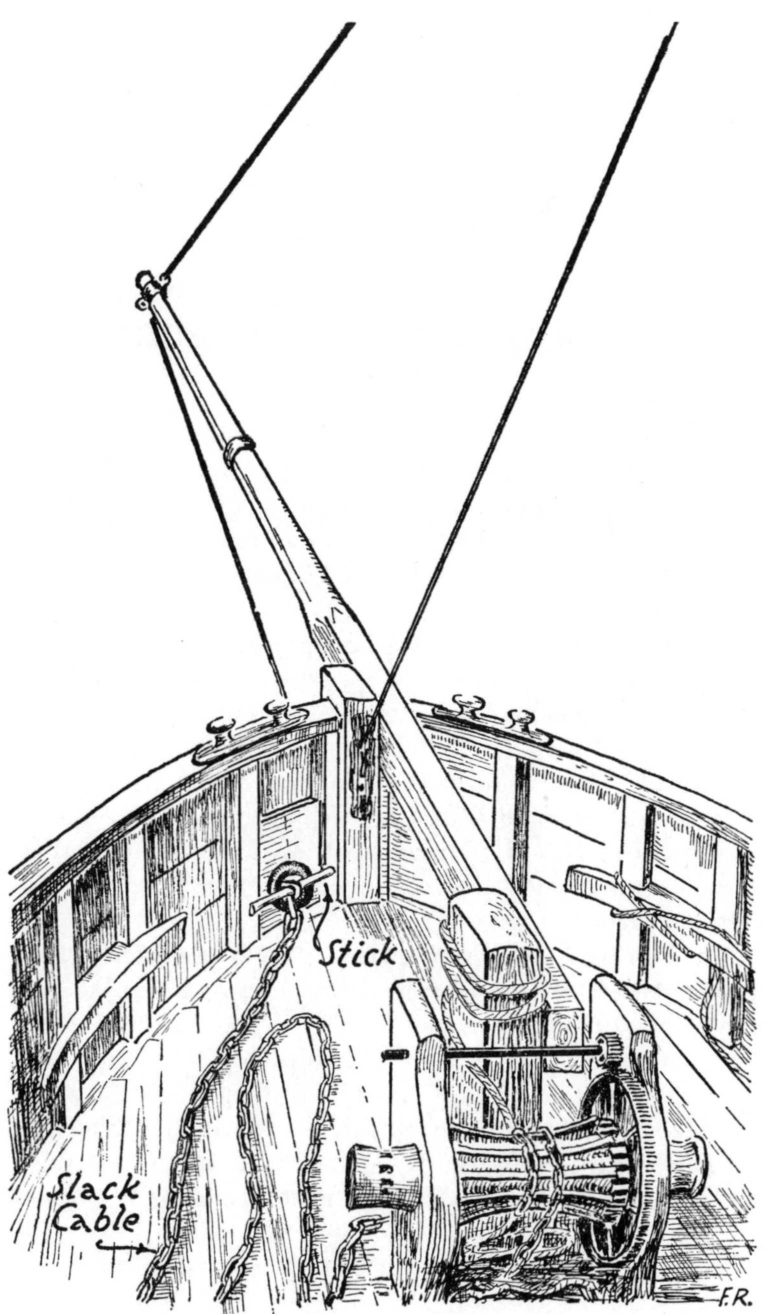

Fig. 15—Trowman's 'alarm-clock'

Chapter 7

PHOTOGRAPHING THE BORE

Being no expert I hesitate to expound on this subject. Nevertheless I am prompted to offer a few hints.

Although a modern camera winds on quickly, the bore remains largely a 'one shot' subject; you make your exposure and the thing is gone—and goodness knows when you'll have another chance.

The important thing is to realise that we are photographing not a landscape but a stretch of open water. The land is but a frame. We are photographing almost entirely the reflection of the sky in a distorting mirror, so must expose and use filters accordingly. Before this dawned on me I blazed away whole films on mountainous seascapes when sailing, only to secure pictures of mill-pond calm, or nearly so. Too often the same thing happens with bore photographs; the waves simply refuse to come out.

The best bore photograph I know (No. 4) was taken below Lower Parting by the late Mr W. Chubb of Gloucester in September 1921. I never met Mr Chubb, but have heard he tried for years before securing this superb picture and even then admitted lots of luck. A study of the photograph is rewarding. Note how the general landscape is in silhouette. Mr Chubb exposed for the sky, not the land; we see the little cloud clearly reflected before the wave disturbs the mirror calmness of the water.

Next, the picture shows the need to photograph against the light, towards a bright sky. The foreground vegetation is backlighted, and the bright edge of the reflected cloud also betrays the sun's approximate direction. Obviously the darker sky was above or behind the camera. The shading of the sloping surface of each wave arises from the mirror being tilted, as it were, to reflect this darker zone while the ridges and nearer water reflect in contrast the brighter sky ahead. Fig. 16 illustrates the point, also how the reverse situation reduces contrast to a minimum.

Another useful hint can be learned from Mr Chubb's

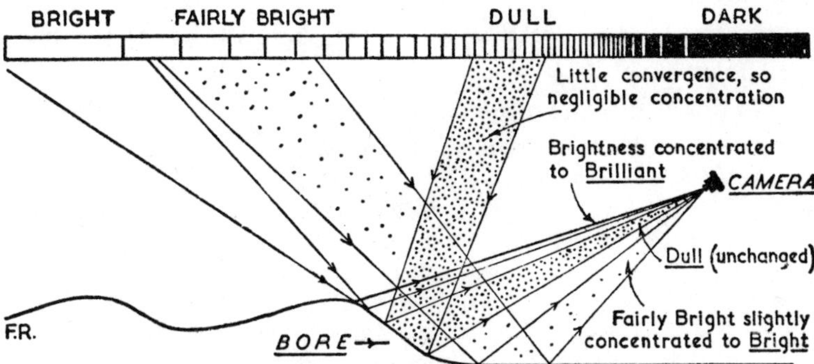

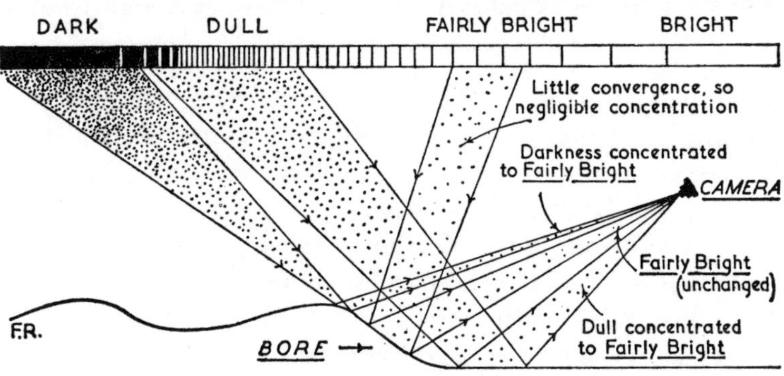

Fig. 16—A guide to photographing the bore

photograph. As we watch in our view-finders a bore approaching from a distance it reaches a point of nearness when it fills the width of our picture. Then we usually 'click'. But Mr Chubb allowed it to advance till more than half the leading wave had passed out of vision to the right, yet we have the impression of seeing the whole bore. We lose little, but gain much in detail, contrast and general interest. When the bore is remote our line of vision is so flat that all reflected light comes from the same zone of sky, so there is little contrast and the waves do not show up (Fig. 17). Furthermore, from this angle the leading wave screens those behind. So let the bore get fairly near.

Do not climb down the bank. This not only flattens the line of vision but places you in great danger. My friend Frank

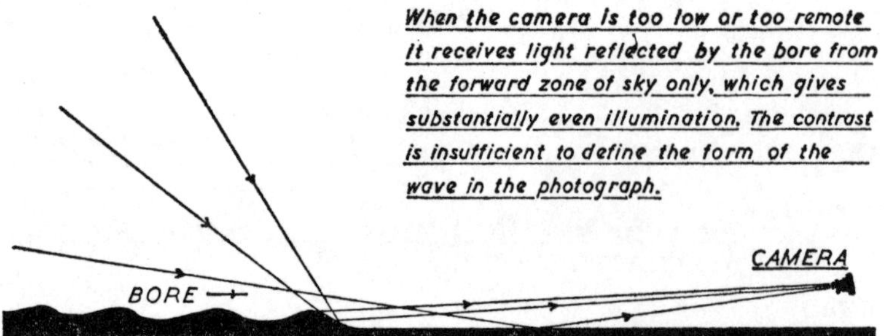

Fig. 17—Don't take the picture too soon

Chamberlayne had a drenching and a narrow escape from death when he took the extraordinary view in Plate 10. With all respect to Frank this is virtually a freak and I know he agreed, Mr. Chamberlayne having died since the last edition. As a general rule the higher the viewpoint the better. Good pictures can be obtained when the bore is sweeping round a bend, preferably when more than halfway round, for then the wave has swung over to the outside bank and is accentuated.

Unless you are well aloft the 'passing' shot is your only chance of taking a near view of the width of the bore. Yet I find this prone to yield remarkable and unexpected results.

Unless the wave is breaking or the water etched with wind ripples, there is only the reflection of the opposite shore to indicate the form. This can be grotesquely distorted.

A rear view of the bore is rarely good unless you catch the instant it meets a tump and hurls aloft a cloud of spray. Better to be in front of such a tump than just behind it! In any event never use a tump as your grandstand; not only will you and your camera be drenched but the tump itself may be smashed from beneath your feet. Always look after your precious camera, especially if you are in a boat. Peter Purves and camera-man Bob McShane of the B.B.C. Blue Peter team lost a £1,500 camera when they were capsized by the bore and another was lost though later recovered when a Dr. Who sequence was being filmed at Westbury Strand.

We were discussing 'stills', but most of my hints can be adapted to cine technique. Yet for cine enthusiasts I would add one more. If using a spring-driven camera try to resist the temptation to start a continuous shot from the moment the distant bore rolls into sight; the motor is sure to run down just as the bore reaches its best position, and it won't pause for you to re-wind! In any event distant shots are not very effective, as has been explained.

When I first rode the bore for B.B.C. television, Producer Ron Webster, using a spring-driven camera on the shore, had his motor run down on him just before bore met boat. His quick re-wind mechanism soon put him in action again, but the very climax had been missed.

Probably I thought myself up to date in applying modern techniques to my studies when I first filmed the bore in cine in 1935. But later I discovered that the bore was one of the first of movie stars, having had its performance at Stonebench cinematographed under the direction of that great pioneer of tidal study, Dr Vaughan Cornish, on the morning of 29 September 1901.

SUMMARY OF FACTS & FIGURES

NUMBER OF BORES PER ANNUM: Approximately 260, i.e., 2 per day on about 130 days. Large bores on about 25 days, morning and evening.

BORE TIDES: All tides of 8 metres or over on the Sharpness gauge have bores when river conditions are normal. Large bores occur with tides over 9.5 metres at Sharpness.

HEIGHT OF BORE: Can be 3 metres in mid-stream, but 1 metre is good. Height at banks much greater than in mid-stream and further accentuated on outer banks of bends.

WIDTH OF BORE: In sandy estuary width is unconfined and variable up to 250 metres. Minsterworth to Gloucester, bank to bank, 80 to 95 metres.

SPEED OF BORE: In sandy estuary 8 to 13 kilometres per hour according to location. Minsterworth to Gloucester 16 to 21 kilometres per hour.

SPEED OF WATER: Near Sharpness maximum flood and ebb 9.5 kilometres per hour. Minsterworth to Gloucester flood ebb 8 kilometres per hour; both considerably affected by freshwater flows.

BORE SEASONS: Bores occur all the year round with spring tides, but are biggest near an equinox.

Vernal Equinox: February—March—April
Autumnal Equinox: August—September—October

BORE DATES: Maximum bores occur one to three days after new and full moons; smaller ones on days immediately preceding and following maxima.

BORE TIMES: Between 7 a.m. and noon; 7 p.m. and midnight. Largest between 9 o'clock and 11 o'clock morning and evening (G.M.T.). Individual times determined from tide tables.

LENGTH OF TRAVEL: Awre to Gloucester—33.8 kilometres.

TIME OF TRAVEL: 2 hrs. 10 mins. to 2 hrs. 35 mins. according to conditions.

FACTORS AFFECTING HEIGHT AND TIME OF BORE

(in addition to height and time of H.W. at Sharpness)

Bore height INCREASED by:

i. Strong west to south-west winds
ii. About 0.75 metres of freshwater below Gloucester
iii. Channels of estuary well scoured
iv. Low barometer

Bore height DECREASED by:

i. Strong north to east winds
ii. Absence of freshwater
iii. Too much freshwater
iv. High barometer

Bore made EARLIER by:

i. Strong west to south-west winds
ii. Up to 15 metres of freshwater
iii. Channels cutting shorter routes through estuary sands
iv. Channels well scoured
v. Low barometer

Bore made LATER by:

i. Strong north to east winds
ii. Absence of freshwater
iii. Channels cutting longer routes through estuary sands
iv. Channels unscoured, with high beds
v. High barometer

Note: The strength and direction of the wind out at sea is often of more consequence than prevailing local wind conditions.

INDEX

ACKNOWLEDGMENTS

My general thanks are due to the trowmen, bargemen, fishermen and all my other friends in the community of Severnside who have helped me continuously from my early childhood towards an understanding of the river.

Nor am I unmindful that the course of my daily round of serving the Catchment Board and River Board has been the means of vastly increasing my previous knowledge of the Severn and its tides and has kept me, inevitably, in close contact with many facets of river life and lore which lie outside the scope of my official duties and form a large proportion of the substance of this book.

In the more particular field of producing the book I most gratefully acknowledge the valuable help of my old friend and one-time colleague, Michael Verney, and of Miss Dorothy Harrop, in proffering advice, checking manuscripts and generally urging me on.

My warmest thanks are due also to Miss Rachel Blundell for so beautifully typing the manuscript in double quick time.

FRED ROWBOTHAM